All-Color Guide

Wonders

of the World   **David Carroll**

A Ridge Press Book

Bantam Books
Toronto·New York·London

Photo Credits

AW—Amwest	IB—Image Bank	PA—Peter Arnold
BC—Bruce Coleman	MP—Magnum Photos	SL—Sea Library

Said Abuhamdeh: 104; Jim Adams (AW): 17 (btm. rt.); Air India: 107 (left); Helmut Albrecht (BC): 56; American Museum of Natural History: 24, 115 (btm. left); C. Anderson (SL): 41 (btm.); A.T.&T. Photo Center: 125; Australia News & Information Bureau: 38; Jen & Des Bartlett: 55 (btm.), 61 (top & btm.); Rattaello Bencini, (Scala): 81; Federico Borromeo (Scala): 82, 83, 93, 107 (rt.), 153; British Museum: 145, 149; Harry Brocke: 139; Peter Buckley: 16–17 (btm. left), 26, 84, 85, 88, 89, 90 (top & btm.), 108, 116; René Burri (MP): 106, 143; David Carroll: 92; Mitchell Carter: 33; G. Clough (BC): 73; Bruce Coleman: 64, 68; Ed Cooper: 34, 35, 50; Geofrey Cove (IB): 135; A. J. Deane (BC): 67; Dept. of Agriculture: 62; N. DeVore III (BC): 55 (top rt.), 72; Robert L. Dunne (BC): 63; J. L. Ebeling (BC): 60; Editorial Archives: 36; F. Erize (BC): 60; Exxon Corp: 44; John Flannery (BC): 23; M.P.L. Fogden (BC): 70; J. Foott (BC): 58; C. Gilbert (SL): 41 (top); J. Gilbert: 126; Burt Glinn (MP): 43; Hale Observatories: 138; C. Haycraft (AW): 31; Grant Hielman: 116, 137; José Honnorez (BC): 16–17 (top); Jacques Jangoux: 29, 75 (btm.), 111; Bill Noel Kleeman (Tom Stack & Assoc.): 123; S. J. Kraseman (PA): 53, 66; Fred Lord (AW): 19; Svat Macha (AW): 20, 47, 52, 86; Metropolitan Museum of Art, New York: 42 (Howard Mansfield Collection, Rogers Fund), 140–141 (btm. left), 148 (Cloisters Collection), 151 (Gift of Alexander Smith Cochran), 154 (Munsey Bequest); Norman Meyers (BC): 57; David Namias: 115 (btm. rt.), 118–119, 121, 122; NASA: 18, 136; National Broadcasting Corp: 134; National Museum of New Delhi: 141 (btm. rt.); National Museum of Tokyo: 152; New York Public Library, Prints Division: 7, 8, 11, 14, 15; Jack Novak (DeWys, Inc.): 21; Old Sturbridge Village, Mass: 132; Oriental Institute, Univ. of Chicago: 124; O.S.F. (BC): 54 (top left); George Rodger (MP): 76; Richard Rowan: 75 (top rt.), 78, 79, 94, 96–97; Leonard Lee Rue III (BC): 27; Runk & Schoenberger (Grant Hielman): 51; Al Satterwhite (IB): 69; Scala: 100, 141 (top), 143, 144, 154, 155, 156; G. B. Schaller (BC): 48; Everett Short: 75 (top left), 99 (top & btm.); Bruce D. Silverstein (PA): 113; Clyde H. Smith (PA): 45; Smithsonian Institution: 118, 120; Albert Squillace: 9, 77, 95, 109, 115 (center), 127, 139; Stearns Magnetics: 37; J. Stewart (BC): 28; John L. Stage (IB): 102, 103; W. Story (BC): 49; Marty Stouffer (BC): 65; Stouffer Productions (BC): 55 (center rt.), 59; David Sumner (AW): 39, 46; N. K. Temnikow (SL): 32; R. Thompson (BC): 71; Pete Turner (IB): 87, 112; United States Air Force: 115 (top); University of California, Berkeley: 25; Luis Villota (IB): 105: Waugh (PA): 80, 101.

Front cover: Angkor ruins, Bayon temple, Cambodia; Richard Rowan

Back cover: Victoria Falls, Rhodesia; G. Harrison (BC) Title page: Persepolis ruins; Scala

---

WONDERS OF THE WORLD

A Bantam Book published by arrangement with The Ridge Press, Inc.

Designed and produced by The Ridge Press, Inc. All rights reserved.

Copyright 1976 in all countries of the International Copyright Union by The Ridge Press, Inc. This book may not be reproduced in whole or in part by mimeograph or any other means, without permission.

For information address: The Ridge Press, Inc.,

25 West 43rd Street, New York, N.Y. 10036

Library of Congress Catalog Card Number: 76-27575

ISBN 0-553-02897-9

Published simultaneously in the United States and Canada.

Bantam Books are published by Bantam Books, Inc.

Its trademark, consisting of the words "Bantam Books" and the portrayal of a bantam, is registered in the United States Patent Office and in other countries. Marca Registrada.

Bantam Books, Inc., 666 Fifth Avenue, New York, N.Y. 10019

Printed in Italy by Mondadori Editore, Verona

Contents

Introduction

What is a wonder of the world? It can be any object that we have marveled at through the ages, any force that has introduced profound improvements to our lives, any creation of man or nature that changes the world.

This book takes a look at some of these wonders great and small. Naturally it is a sampling, for to cover all the fabulous things of the world would take more volumes than are found in a king's library. This sampling, however, is a representative one. It draws both from the marvels of nature and from the art and ingenuities of mankind. For example, the electric light is one kind of wonder and the rose is another.

To qualify as a wonder, size may be a factor. A person standing next to the statue of Buddha in the Bamiyan Valley of Afghanistan will scarcely be able to see over its foot. Magnitude of power, too, can be important: when the volcano Krakatoa erupted in 1883 its force was greater than that of three hydrogen bombs. And yet a tiny creature such as the honeybee, which performs the important fuction of pollination, also has a profound effect on the world. Thus it is not necessarily size and splendor that constitute the subject of this book. It is anything that arouses astonishment, awe, change, surprise, and perhaps above all admiration in us—admiration for our life and for the earth that sustains it.

Seven Wonders of the Ancient World

The famous Seven Wonders of the World were first described for posterity by one Antipater of Sidon in the second century B.C. Antipater listed seven great temples, monuments, and tombs, each of them widely revered throughout ancient society. Of these seven wonders only one remains today, the Pyramids of Egypt. The rest are known in fragments or not at all, their legends handed down through the centuries in historical texts and by word of mouth.

The Colossus of Rhodes, Gobelins Tapestry, France ▶

The Pyramids of Egypt

Though there were many pyramids in the Nile Valley of Egypt, those of kings Kafre, Menkaure, and Cheops (Khufu), near Giza, are the most famous and enduring. Of the original Seven Wonders of the World they are the only structures still standing.

No one knows how ancient these monuments really are. Some have claimed them to be 10,000 years or older, though the accepted theory is that the greatest of them was built in 3700 B.C. by King Cheops. This pyramid, built of stone, is some 750 feet (230 m) square and is as high as a forty-story office building. In its central part lies a sinuous passageway that leads to the burial chamber of its builder. The 2,300,000 blocks used in the pyramid—each weighing 2.5 tons (2.27 M tons)—were transported to the building site at a rate of 300 blocks a day. Though these blocks are today exposed, giving the pyramid its characteristic stepped appearance, it was once faced with limestone slabs, making each of its four sides perfectly smooth. This outer casing was later removed by Arabs, who used it to build the palaces and mosques of Cairo.

DIANÆ TEMPLVM

Temple of Diana at Ephesus

Ephesus lies on the eastern shore of the Aegean Sea. A mile from its city gates once stood a magnificent edifice dedicated to Diana the Huntress (the Greek Artemis). This great goddess was the personification of organic life (she was equated with an early native nature and fertility goddess) and was worshipped here in this capacity by devotees throughout Greece. Diana's temple, the Roman scholar Pliny relates, occupied over 80,000 square feet (7,432 sq. m) of ground and was surrounded by lawns and groves of trees. It measured 400 feet (122 m) in length, 200 feet (61 m) in width, and was considered the most perfect of all Greek temples. Built in the Ionic style, it was supported by 127 columns on top of which rested a polychromed entablature depicting scenes from Greek religion. The building was started in 550 B.C. and was half completed when Alexander the Great stopped there on his march to Asia. The conqueror offered to finance its completion if his name could be inscribed on the base. "It is not fitting," the people of Ephesus diplomatically replied, "that one god should build a temple for another god," and a flattered Alexander continued on his way. The temple stood until 260 A.D. when it was razed by the Goths. A thousand years later when Crusaders arrived from the west they asked to see the great edifice, but the townspeople could not oblige. They no longer remembered that such a monument had ever been built. **9**

Lighthouse at Pharos

Legend tells that an architect named Sostratus of Cnidus lived in Alexandria, Egypt, in 280 B.C. The architect was betrothed to a girl from a distant land. But on the night of her arrival a great wind blew the ship off course, and because the Alexandrian coast had no beacon, the vessel was lost at sea. Vowing to construct a tower that would spare others from such tragedy, Sostratus chose a small island, Pharos, off the mainland. He received unlimited funds from the Egyptian king, Ptolemy II, and began building a giant lighthouse there, the first in recorded history. The lighthouse was constructed of white marble and stood 440 feet high (134 m). It was built in three sections, the bottom part being a square block, the second an octagonal tower, and the third a cylindrical turret with windows that faced the sea. Out of each of these windows shone the light of an enormous fire; it was a beacon to mariners for almost a thousand years until earthquakes and bands of **10** marauders destroyed it sometime during the Middle Ages.

Hanging Gardens of Babylon

Forty miles from Baghdad, Iraq, on the banks of the Euphrates River, can be seen the ruins of Babylon, the "Gate of God." From 604 to 561 B.C. the ruler of this great metropolis was Nebuchadnezzar, a king famous for rebuilding Babylon and making it the most regal city of ancient times. One of his most awe-inspiring creations was the Hanging Garden that he built for his queen from Media, Amytis. Greek historians have left us descriptions of this wondrous garden, called "hanging" because it was built in a series of stepped square tiers that seemed to float above the ground. Each of these tiers held a garden terrace filled with exotic plantings, marble statues, lime trees, pines, wild birds imported from North Africa, and flowerbeds irrigated by a reservoir situated on the uppermost tier. Marble banquet chambers were stationed on every terrace, and each was filled with date palms and decorated with mosaics depicting tales of the gods. The buildings were surrounded by lawns, pavilions for music and dance, and swimming ponds in which the water was colored red, gold, or blue, according to the day of the week. In this paradisiacal landscape, tradition says, the queen, who so longed for the forests and hills of her native land, was made to feel at home.

Mausoleum at Halicarnassus

Around 550 B.C. Mausolos reigned over the kingdom of Caria in Asia Minor with his queen (and sister), Artemisia. When this powerful potentate died his bereaved wife decided to build him the largest tomb ever known in the ancient world. The four best artists of the day were summoned to the city of Halicarnassus and work began. The first artist, Brayaxis, constructed the north side of the tomb; the second, Timotheus, the south; Leochares, the west; and the great Scopas, the east. Copies of

the plans for this monument still exist, showing that the king was placed in a central burial chamber over which a 140-foot (43-m) tower was erected. This tower was built in the Ionic style, decorated with 36 columns, and topped by a magnificent frieze depicting the mythical battle between the Amazons and the Greeks. On top of the frieze was a pyramid-shaped roof crowned by a statue of the royal couple driving a chariot. The tomb was destroyed in the Middle Ages by an earthquake, but its name lives on in the word "mausoleum." **13**

Colossus of Rhodes

The Colossus of Rhodes, a towering figure of Helios the Greek sun god, was built between 292 and 280 B.C. It was cast entirely of bronze, and stood 170 feet (52 m) from pedestal to crown. Its hollow body had a spiral staircase inside, allowing a person to ascend to the head from where a view of the harbor could be enjoyed. Inspiration for its construction came when the army of Demetrius I (Poliocretes), the "Besieger," was driven away from the gates of Rhodes, leaving behind its bronze machinery of war. In gratitude to Helios for deliverance, the townspeople melted the weapons and from them built this giant figure, entrusting its design to Chares of Lindus. So attached did Lindus become to his masterpiece, legend tells, that when criticized about a fine point in its construction he committed suicide on the spot. The statue took twelve years to build and stood only half a century before it was snapped in half by an earthquake. It lay on the ground for another 800 years, until its bronze debris—200 tons (181.4 M tons) of it—were carted away by a caravan of camels. Today the statue lives on in the word "colossal."

Statue of Zeus at Olympia

In the ancient Greek town of Olympia stood a sacred grove where the Olympic Games were held every four years and where special homage was paid to the greatest of the gods, Zeus. Though many sanctuaries adorned Olympus, the most noted was the Temple of Zeus, designed by the architect Libon of Elis. Inside, a masterful statue of the king of gods stood in the west end of the building directly facing the entranceway, so that upon entering the shrine a worshiper could behold it through a long double row of columns. The statue of Zeus was the work of Phidias of Athens, greatest of all Greek sculptors. Phidias spent four years carving the statue, modeling it after Homer's description of Zeus in *The Iliad*. The result was a 40-foot (12.3-m) figure seated on a cedarwood throne, its body of ivory and its drapery of gold and precious gems. In Zeus's right hand was a figure of Victory and in his left a giant jeweled scepter. The statue was thought to be so holy that it was veiled by a large curtain and displayed only on sacred days. In 427 A.D. the Temple of Zeus was destroyed. Whether the statue perished then or later in Constantinople is not known.

2 Wonders of the Natural World

Through the centuries some of man's most basic views of nature have changed. To ancient man, nature was a mysterious force, unconquerable and all-powerful. Man then believed that all nature was alive, even the rocks and the waters. But with our technological advancements many such notions have been discarded. We are learning more about the workings of nature, and from this knowledge we have been able to harness and utilize some of its wonders. Still, however, many of nature's complexities remain a mystery to us. There are still many people who perceive a kind of animation and rhythm in each wonder of nature and its relationship to another. These wonders serve as lessons for man's own life, and man in his desire to conquer the world around him must not forget that he, too, is a link in nature's chain.

Sahara Desert ▼ Mt. Etna, Sicily ▲ Giant Sequoia ▼

Polar Lights

One of the familiar and beautiful sights in the higher latitudes is the aurora polaris, the polar lights. In the northern regions it is known as the aurora borealis, or "northern lights," and in the south, aurora australis, the later being sighted (officially) for the first time by Captain Cook in 1773. The polar lights extend from 65 to 500 miles (105–805 km) above the earth, and can usually be seen only in the far north or south. Polar light can be seen in autumn and winter, occurring at opposite times at the two poles. It sometimes appears as colored rays, sometimes as arcs of flame, sometimes as great auroral coronas sweeping the sky. Modern science believes that polar light is created by the entrance into the upper atmosphere of mysterious charged particles from the sun. These particles collide with the atoms and molecules in the upper air. The atoms and molecules are forced into a downward spiral along the lines of the earth's magnetic field, and in their descent they cause atmospheric gases to emit light. By passing an electrical current through rarefied gases this same effect has often been reproduced in the laboratory, thus giving the charged-particle theory substantial verification.

Aurora borealis through the window of NASA aircraft ▲

Roses

For countless centuries the rose has been one of the most treasured flowers. This is the case not only because of its beauty, variety, and alluring scent, but because its perennial stock produces blooms all summer long, a rare quality in any flowering plant. Botanically the rose belongs to the family *Rosaceae,* which hybridizes easily and produces so many diverse species that it is often difficult to determine the parent stock. Roses can be erect, climbing, or trailing. All three kinds have thorned stems and aromatic leaves pinnately arranged. Although roses are particularly popular in the United States and Europe, about 80 percent are native to Asia. Most types were brought to the West by Arabs during the time of the Crusades and quickly became the symbol of both religious ardor and romantic love. Through the centuries roses have served a practical as well as ornamental use. They are used in perfumes, soaps, potpourris, and cosmetics. The hips from the flower are an excellent source of vitamin C, and as a confection the candied petals are delicious.

Death Valley

Of all the desert wildernesses in the United States, the hottest (readings of 135°F [57°C] have been recorded in summer), the lowest (over 500 square miles [1,300 sq km] are below sea level), and the driest (annual rainfall is only about two inches [5 cm] a year) is Death Valley. Located in southeast California almost on the California-Nevada border, it is bounded on the west by the Panamint Range and on the east by the Black and Funeral ranges. The Valley was declared a national monument in 1933 and now serves to protect many rare natural features, including unique forms of cacti and succulents, several endangered species of animals and birds, a petrified forest, remarkable fossil remains, and some of the only true desert sand dunes in the United States. Also in the Valley are rich deposits of natural resources, gold and borax being the most abundant.

Dubbed Death Valley by explorers on the way to California, the area was first settled in the 1870s by goldminers. In the early part of the twentieth century it became popular with film stars as a winter resort, and today, despite its scorching temperatures, over half a million people a year visit it.

The Blue Grotto

Eighteen miles (30 km) off the mainland near Naples, Italy, is the famous Isle of Capri, a playground for visitors since the time of the Romans. Capri's towering cliffs drop precipitously to the sea and are honeycombed with limestone caves at their base. At one time the so-called Blue Grotto was just another of these many caves with an entranceway large enough to accommodate a sizeable Roman skiff. Then around 500 A.D. an earthquake sank the island 50 feet (15 m) into the sea, reducing the Grotto's entrance and causing a marvelous phenomenon to take place. For the Grotto was now situated in such a relationship to the sunlight that whenever its rays passed through the blue water and into the cave, the reflections produced a mysterious, luminiscent blue light, the principle being the same as that of light passing through stained-glass. Thus the water, rocks, and walls seem to be aflame with shimmering blue reflections, and at the same time the water below appears as shimmering silver. This haunting effect has long captured the wonder of man, and for centuries the Grotto was considered a holy place.

Rivers

One of mankind's most treasured natural resources is the river. Ancient civilizations settled along river shores not only for agricultural purposes but because rivers provided transportation, drinking water, minerals, and boundary delineation. Eons before Christ, the Chinese lived and prospered along the Yangtze and Yellow rivers. Western civilization first dawned near the confluence of the Tigris and Euphrates. In Egypt the Nile was the focus of all life, and many river deities adorned the Egyptian pantheon of gods. At various times of the year the Nile flooded, leaving rich deposits of minerals and plant debris making agriculture possible and hence civilization in an otherwise uninhabitable terrain.

A river is a substantial body of water flowing on a prescribed course through defined channels or riverbeds. Its ultimate destination is usually, but not always, the sea. A river can be fed from several sources that usually start as tributaries and eventually join up to form the main body of the river. The rivers of Canada, the Alps, Siberia, and eastern Europe are all created by streams of melting snow. The Rhône in France and the Ganges in India are products of glaciers melting high in their respective mountain ranges, the Alps and the Himalayas. The Seine in France—a so-called "pluvial" river—is fed by rains, ground water, and general atmospheric precipitation.

In geological terms a river can be young, mature, or old. A young river moves swiftly down a steep gradient with few tributaries adding to its flow—the Colorado River is such an example. After long periods of erosion rivers become mature; their movement is more leisurely and they meander through wide valleys and mountain plateaus. Finally an old river, such as the White River in the Missouri Ozarks, is one that flows lazily over a flat, worn plain.

Though the Nile or the Mississippi is often thought to be the longest river in the world, the true champion is the Amazon in South America. Not only does it extend farther than any river on earth, measuring 4,195 miles (7,102 km) from its source in Peru to its mouth in Brazil, but it averages the greatest volume flow as well, discharging some 4,200,000 cubic feet (118,931 cu m) of water into the Atlantic Ocean every second of the day.

Bear River, Utah and Wyoming ▶

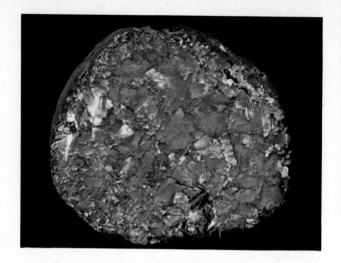

Gems

Through history, gems have been precious to man both as ornaments and as a means of concentrating wealth. Like all minerals, a gem is a combination of chemical elements formed by natural geological processes. What qualifies it specifically as a gem is its rarity, durability, and above all, its beauty. Thus, of the 2,000 or so minerals only 16 have gem status: diamond, feldspar, beryl (includes emerald and aquamarine), chrysoberyl, olivine, quartz, zircon, turquoise, topaz, corundum (includes sapphire and ruby), garnet, lazulite, opal, tourmaline, spinel, and jade. In their natural state many of these gems must be identified by experts who test for form, fracture, cleavage, crystal, and hardness; only after they are cut and polished do their pleasing qualities emerge. Cutting is done in three ways: cabochon (rounded or curved surfaces), carved (intaglio and relief), and faceted (multiple flat surfaces). In modern times the color of precious stones is sometimes controlled by the use of cathode rays and radium emanations. Diamonds can be given a green coloration and agates are sometimes internally stained with dyes. Gems in their pure, unchanged state, however, are **24** for the majority of collectors far more valuable and appealing.

Black Opal ▲ Earthquake in Dasht-i-Biaz, Iran; 1968 ▶

Earthquakes

Since the beginning of civilization, people have lived in fear and awe of earthquakes. In the Middle Ages, Biblical prophesies of a world-destroying quake were awaited by the pious, and in 1755, when the great earthquake of Lisbon took 10,000 lives in six minutes, many thought the predictions had finally come to pass. An earthquake is the result of geological forces—thermal heat, volcanic activity, and underground pressures—which place stress on rock masses and finally cause them to rupture, setting up vibrations called seismic waves, which shake the earth. The result of these vibrations can be catastrophic, not only irreversibly deforming the landscape and costing many lives and millions of dollars in damage, but setting up secondary effects such as landslides and tidal waves that often do more harm than the quake itself. To predict the coming of these destructive events science has developed the seismograph, a highly sensitive machine capable of charting seismic vibrations throughout the world. Whenever an earthquake occurs these machines measure its shock waves and are able to predict the appearance of a quake hours and sometimes days in advance.

The Sahara Desert
The Sahara is the largest desert in the world, taking up one-third of the continent of Africa. Though its temperatures reach a blistering 135°F (57°C) in certain regions and its rainfall is less than six inches (15 cm) a year, during the Ice Ages it was a fertile plain, laced with rivers and covered with grass. The Sahara, whose name in Arabic means "wilderness," is composed of three different terrains: the *erg*, a vast expanse of shifting sand dunes, void of water and vegetation; the *reg*, an arid, rocky plain where an occasional oasis dots the landscape, and animals—badgers, snakes, wild goats, and antelope—scratch out a meager subsistence; and the *hamada*, stony plateaus with dry river valleys and some vegetation. Three main tribes inhabit these regions: Taureg nomads of central Sahara, the Tebu of the east, and the Moors of the west. They farm, raise animals, and struggle for survival in one of the most forbidding environments.

Victoria Falls

Victoria Falls are located on the border between the South African countries of Rhodesia and Zambia. Though they are not, as is often believed, the largest waterfalls in the world (this distinction belongs to the Guaira on the Alto Parana River between Brazil and Paraguay) they are by many accounts the most majestic. Situated midway along the Zambesi River, the falls plunge into a chasm some 350 feet (107 m) deep, producing an awesome cloud of vapor from which its native name *Mosi-wa-Tunya* (meaning "roaring cloud") is derived. The volume of water passing over the great falls is enormous, sometimes reaching 70 million gallons (265 million liters) a minute. This volume cascades furiously against the opposite wall of the chasm falls, then passes out a narrow channel known as the "Boiling Pot." Victoria Falls were discovered in 1855 by the English explorer, David Livingstone, who named them for his Queen. Today the area is a national park jointly maintained by the governments of Rhodesia and Zambia.

Thunder and Lightning

Thunder and lightning are the result of severe disturbances in the atmosphere. An incipient thunderstorm is composed of many small cumulus clouds called "cells." Warm air from the lower atmosphere spirals upward through these cells. At a certain point the cool upper atmosphere causes the air's temperature to fall below dew level and the moisture quickly condenses, transforming the individual cumulus cells into those dark, threatening thunderheads that mark the coming of a storm. When the thunderhead's load of condensed moisture receives the powerful electrical charge present in the atmosphere, it is discharged as rain. When the cloud draws near the earth, which carries its own equal and opposite electrical charge, a positive-negative attraction is set up and a huge spark or electrical discharge passes between heaven and earth—lightning. The force of this electrical discharge then vaporizes all local airborne moisture, expanding the air and causing a partial vacuum to develop. When the surrounding air rushes violently back into the vacuum, a familiar crashing **28** sound is heard across the landscape—thunder.

Orchids

Orchids are some of the most exotic and unusual members of the plant kingdom. They come in all colors—some having as many as seven different hues—and in an astonishing variety of shapes and sizes. There are an estimated 30,000 orchid varieties, some existing in temperate zones and a few in colder regions where they grow as herbs or shrubs. However, they are most numerous in the higher mountain rain forests of the world, commonly found in the foothills of the Andes and Himalayas, the jungles of Central America and Mexico, and perhaps above all in the Malaysian archipelago.

Orchids normally thrive among rocks and trees. They are parasitic, with aerial roots that cling to the bark of trees. When artificially cultivated they are usually bred for purposes of sales and hobby. Indeed, since the invention of the modern greenhouse they have become a multimillion-dollar industry among florists and horticulturists. The dried tubers of the *Orchis* variety, however, are still used in parts of the Middle East as a sedative, and the cured, unripened pods of the *Vanilla planifoliais* remain an excellent source of natural vanilla. **29**

▲ Orchidaceae in Venezuela

The Ocean

The sea comprises over three-fifths of the earth's surface and is one of the primary sources of life on our planet. Its effects on weather and climate are profound. As a source of food it is vast, though not unlimited as was believed in preecological years. It is a source of chemicals, minerals, boundary delineation, recreation, waste disposal, travel, and of late has become important as a supplier of petroleum. Coal, natural gas, precious gems, salt for our tables—all are but a few of its innumerable treasures.

Though the ocean is one continuous expanse of water, geographers arbitrarily divide it into five smaller bodies: the Pacific, Atlantic, Indian, Arctic, and Antarctic oceans. The Pacific is by far the largest, taking up one half of the earth's water surface, followed by the Atlantic, the Indian, and finally the two polar seas. Inland bodies of water such as the Caspian and the Baltic also bear the name of sea but these are not considered part of the ocean proper.

Sea water has a greenish blue hue and carries some three **30** pounds of salt to every hundred pounds of water. This lowers

its freezing point to 28.7°F, (−1.8°C) though marine water temperatures vary enormously, raising as high as 90°F (32°C) in areas around the Persian Gulf. Beneath the surface the ocean floor is as diversified as its continental counterpart, including shelves, submarine canyons, plains, mountains, marine deserts, and valleys. Its most remarkable topographical features are its enormous trenches, the deepest located in the South Pacific. The Mariana Trench is estimated to be some 35,000 feet (10,670 m) in depth and the Kuril-Kamchatka, 34,000 (10,360 m).

Ocean water is in a continual state of circulation, just like the bloodstream of man (to which, incidentally, it bears an astonishing chemical resemblance). The first reason for this activity is the currents, caused by changes in water temperatures and shifting tides. Second are waves, caused mostly by the surface action of the winds. Finally there are tides, periodic risings and fallings of sea level caused by the gravitational pull of the sun and moon. Despite this ceaseless activity, marine life sustains itself on all levels of the ocean, and scarcely a drop of sea water does not contain some form of aquatic life. **31**

Polar Ice Caps

The earth is crowned on opposite ends by large ice caps known as the North and South poles. The South Pole, Antarctica, is far larger than its northern counterpart and is geologically ranked as a separate continent. Along its shores run rugged mountain peaks, while inland are vast expanses of ice and glaciated terrain. The continent is divided by the Transantarctic Mountains—to the east is a continuous land mass, to the west an ice-bound archipelago. Because of its incredible cold (temperatures of −95°F (−70°C) are sometimes recorded in the interior) life is concentrated in the somewhat warmer coastal regions, where birds and seals occasionally roost. Inland, only mosses, fungi, and a few hardy insect species are capable of survival.

The North Pole, or Arctic Region, is more familiar to man and slightly more hospitable in the southern section, where summer brings thaws, vegetable growth, and temperatures above 60°F (16°C). Here Eskimo and Siberian tribesmen hunt and fish for survival, and natural resources are mined. In the far north in the area around the pole, however, only ice and snow prevail, making this perhaps the most desolate spot on earth.

Rainbows

A rainbow is a luminous, iridescent arch that appears in clouds or fog opposite the sun. In the seventeenth century science determined it to be a phenomenon of the refraction of light. Both Descartes and Newton experimented with the rainbow's properties, and from their studies the science of optics was born. They established that a rainbow is formed by the refraction, reflection, and dispersion of sunlight through water vapor. When seen from a certain angle this sunlight becomes separated into its component spectrum colors: violet, indigo, blue, green, yellow, orange, and red. A rainbow is the result. The same phenomenon can be reproduced by passing light through a prism or by heating certain metals until they glow.

A typical rainbow consists of two concentric arches, the inner one called a *primary bow,* and the outer a *secondary bow.* In the first bow, red is the external color and violet the inner; in secondary bows this sequence is reversed. Rainbows, furthermore, can be observed only when the sun is 40° or less above the horizon, which is why they appear in early morning or late in the day. Although they may sometimes stretch for great distances, only a portion of them can be seen. **33**

Mountains

Mountains are the largest and most grandiose of nature's productions, invariably considered wondrous if not sacred by peoples throughout the world. Geologically speaking, they are created by four different processes. First is volcanic activity, which causes immense cones and shields of solidified lava to be formed. Mt. Etna in Italy and Mt. Lassen in northern California are examples. Second are mountains carved by weathering, erosion, or running water. These regions usually display jagged, jutting peaks; the Beartooth Mountains of Montana are typical. Third are mountains built by the compressive activity of the earth's crust, such as the Himalayas. This constant surging, squeezing pressure causes the earth to buckle into enormous folds. Such a process requires millions of years, but before it is finished the folds may attain heights of five miles (8 km) or more. Finally, there are mountains created by sudden **34** geological upheavals and dislocations, the result of faulting

Mt. Timpanogos, Wasatch Mountains, Utah ▲

and crustal breaks. The Sierra Nevada Range in California was created in this manner.

Many of the earth's majestic mountains belong to the ocean as well as the land. The Virgin Islands in the Caribbean and the Hawaiian Islands are nothing more than the projecting tips of gigantic submarine peaks. In fact, the Hawaiian mountain Mauna Kea, a large portion of which is undersea, has a full height of 33,476 feet (10,200 m) which, when measured from the ocean floor, makes it more than 4,000 feet (1220 m) taller than Mt. Everest. Though mountains seem to be randomly scattered throughout the planet, most major ranges are situated within two relatively narrow strips that run like jagged bands around the earth. The first extends across the Pacific, up the west coasts of South and North America, into Asia, down through New Zealand, and into Antarctica. The second extends across North Africa, southern Europe, Asia Minor, and into Asia. **35**

▲ Sandia Mountains, New Mexico

Rock of Gibraltar

One of the most imposing natural monuments in all of Europe is the Rock of Gibraltar, a massive limestone hump situated at the eastern end of the Strait of Gibraltar and attached to mainland Spain by a long, sandy isthmus. The rock itself rises to a height of 1,400 feet (426 m). At the base of the western side is nestled the town of Gibraltar; on the east a rocky slope falls vertically to the sea. The mountain is honeycombed with natural limestone caves weathered over millions of years, as well as man-made tunnels carved by the British early in the twentieth century to allow communications between the eastern and western slopes. The name Gibraltar comes from the Arabic military leader, Jabal al-Tarik, who conquered the territory in 711 A.D. The rock was known to the Romans who called it *Mons Calpe* and to the Greeks for whom, under the name of "Pillars of Hercules," it represented the limits of the known world. It was first garrisoned by the Spanish under Charles I and later by the British who took it over in 1704 during the War of Spanish Succession. Today the 25,000 people who live on Gibraltar enjoy self-rule but are almost exclusively dependent on import trades, as practically nothing **36** will grow in Gibraltar's rocky soil.

Circular electromagnet used to lift metal scrap ▶

Magnetism

Magnetism is one of the most prevalent forces in nature. It can be found everywhere, from the surface of magnetic ore to inside the human body. Even the earth itself is one immense magnet, with a positive pole, a negative pole, and an electromagnetic field. Its universality notwithstanding, recent theory maintains that magnetism is not a fundamental force in itself but an *effect* of electricity. The idea is that the electron not only circles the atom but rotates on its own axis as well. In nonmagnetic materials the same number of electrons spin in a clockwise direction as in a counterclockwise direction; but in ferromagnetic substances, such as iron and steel, more electrons turn in one direction than the other with the extra "uncompensated" electrons each developing a substantial but undirected magnetic charge. By subjecting this ferromagnetic material to an external magnetic field, i.e., a magnet, these groups of randomly oriented, uncompensated electrons are brought into steady alignment. This gives the electrons uniform direction and thus endows them with magnetic pull. Today magnetism has many uses in industry, science, and medicine.

The Great Barrier Reef

Off the eastern coast of Australia lies one of nature's most exquisite creations, the Great Barrier Reef. This jagged, serpentine ribbon of coral has, with occasional interruptions from rises and drops in sea level, been forming since the Pleistocene Epoch some one million years ago. Like all coral reefs, its indented, sharp-edged topography is formed by lime remains from countless billions of aquatic animals whose bodies have solidified into coral rock. Such an organic building process is a common one in temperate seas, and many other islands in the area are fringed with similar deposits. What makes the Barrier Reef so spectacular is its immense size (more than 1,250 miles [2,010 km] long), its scenic beauty, and its remarkable abundance of colorful, exotic marine life, this last feature unmatched in the world for undersea recreation. The Great Barrier Reef is not a single band of continuous coral, however, but a kind of archipelago of thousands of lesser reefs that loosely connect and follow the continental shelf. These reefs wander as close as 20 miles (32 km) and as far as 200 miles (322 km) off Australia's coast from the Torres Strait to Rockhampton.

Clouds

When warm air evaporates from the earth's surface it rises to the high regions of the atmosphere. There it comes into contact with cold air masses and quickly condenses into tiny droplets of water. The droplets form a mass of vapor similar in many ways to fog—these enormous collections of water particles are known as clouds. The water particles that constitute a cloud are extraordinarily concentrated, forming a substance some 800 times heavier than air. When these droplets expand to a certain size they then fall to earth as snow, hail, or rain.

Though there are ten main cloud categories and numerous subdivisions, the layman cloudwatcher looks for four basic types: cirrus, stratus, nimbus, and cumulus. Cirrus are pure white, feathery, and detached. They are found in the higher atmosphere and are composed mostly of ice particles. Cumulus are thicker and lower flying, with convoluted shapes and broad bases. Nimbus clouds are dense, amorphous, and are often seen in the vicinity of rainbows. Finally, stratus clouds consist of long, laminated bands visible in the early and later parts of the day.

39

The Galapagos Islands

Some 650 miles (1046 km) off the coast of Ecuador lie the Galapagos Islands, an archipelago formed by fourteen volcanic islands plus a string of smaller keys running far out to sea. Though far from being classically beautiful, the islands have a haunting quality: rugged terrain, arid valleys, strange dwarf trees, spiny cacti, and barren lava hills. Nonetheless their principal attraction is their unusual animal life, most notably the giant, spike-backed iguanas that huddle together in large herds across the islands' rocky knolls, and that appear to be living throwbacks to prehistoric times. Other zoological oddities abound here, too: a fish with four eyes, the oldest and largest turtle in the world (called the Galapagos Turtle, which lives more than a hundred years and weighs as much as 600 pounds [272 kg]), an assortment of rare cormorants and albatrosses, and a type of finch that manipulates a branch to procure its food (one of the few animals on earth known to use a tool). This assemblage of unique animal specimens attracted the young naturalist Charles Darwin, while cruising on the ship *Beagle*. His findings here inspired many of the notions he later developed in his theory of natural selection.

▼ Iguana-covered point ▲ Galapagos Turtle ▼ Masked Boobie

Tidal Waves

Whenever a major marine displacement takes place such as an underwater landslide, earthquake, or erupting volcano, the result on the sea is a tidal wave—*tsunami* as it is called in Japan. Huge amounts of sea water are suddenly lifted and dropped, propagating a swell that contains far more water volume than the normal windswept wave. Starting as a swirling mass of water, the *tsunami* quickly elongates, extending sometimes for a length of 500 miles (805 km) as it follows its inexorable course across the ocean. This makes the *tsunami* difficult to recognize on the open sea, for it stands no more than a foot above sea level, often passing under a ship unnoticed. What it lacks in height, however, it makes up for in velocity. It can approach speeds of 430 knots per hour.

When a tidal wave approaches land it has built itself into a literal wall of water. The first sign of its coming is a rapid and unscheduled fall in sea level (on occasion the waters will actually recede to the horizon, and anyone unwise enough to try it could in theory walk five or ten miles out to sea). Then a towering pillar of wave force follows, bringing with it power and destruction. In 1755 half the city of Lisbon, Portugal, was inundated by a wave 50 feet (15 m) high.

The Steppes

The steppes is a name given by the Russians to a vast, arid stretch of land extending across Siberia and into southeastern Europe. This area is characterized by dry, undulating landscapes broken up by ranges of low-lying hills and occasional vegetation. Though there are occasional groves of trees and spots with lush groundcover—especially in the vicinity of riverbeds—they are largely atypical of the terrain. Similar areas in other parts of the world include the veld in South Africa, the pampas in South America, and the prairies of the United States.

The steppes have an annual precipitation of less than 20 inches (51 cm) a year. In the moderate latitudes various desert grasses prevail and are grazed by antelopes, horses, and deer. However, in the colder, drier regions winter brings an end to this sparse vegetation. Mineral deposits abound in the steppes, though the soil—having developed under subhumid conditions—is not rich. Generally the area is better suited for animal husbandry than agriculture, which is why tribes inhabiting the steppes, the Tartars in particular, have always been nomadic. **43**

◀ *The Great Wave at Kanagawa,* by Katsushika Hokusai

Petroleum

Petroleum accounts for half the energy supply of the world; both private and industrial consumption account for more than one billion gallons each day. Petroleum was originally formed millions of years ago by the decomposition of aquatic plant and animal life in prehistoric seas. Great lakes of it are trapped beneath the earth's surface. In its crude form petroleum is a strong-smelling, greenish brown liquid found in many localities throughout the world, including North and South America, Russia, eastern Europe, and the Middle East. Though it does sometimes bubble up through natural channels pushed by the natural gas that inevitably accompanies it, petroleum is ordinarily pumped to the surface by towering rotary drills. It is then transferred to refineries and distilled into gasoline, naphtha, benzine, kerosene, lubricating oils, and paraffin. These substances in turn are used to manufacture plastics, asphalt, fertilizers, petrochemicals, insecticides, rubber, detergents, and countless other materials. Though the existence of petroleum was known to man for centuries, it was only in the nineteenth century that sophisticated refining procedures made distillation feasible.

Meteors

On any clear night, especially in the warmer months, a star-gazer can observe the long, luminous tracks of shooting stars, or meteors. These are small masses of matter that move around the sun in their own orbit and are believed to have originated from disintegrated comets somewhere in the boundless reaches of space. Our knowledge of meteors is confined to those that penetrate the earth's atmosphere. This they do first in the upper regions at speeds of about 45 miles (72 km) per second, usually converting into heat by the friction in the atmosphere and burning themselves out in a spectacular stream of fire before they reach earth. Occasionally a meteor survives its flaming journey and strikes the planet intact, crystallizing at the point of impact into an iron or nickel alloy. Sometimes the velocity of impact is so great that the meteor melts or even vaporizes as it hits, leaving only a violent explosion and gaping hole as evidence of its arrival. The Great Crater in Arizona, almost a mile in diameter and 600 feet (183 m) deep, was caused by such a meteor thousands of years ago, and is representative of similar craters throughout the planet. **45**

Fire

Fire is generated whenever oxygen and a flammable substance combine and then permit combustion. Besides being a basic phenomenon of the physical world, fire is also one of our important tools. It was originally discovered, archeologists believe, by striking flint against a pyrite stone and using the spark for ignition. This probably took place during the Neolithic Age, around 7000 B.C. At first, fire was used to keep man warm, to cook his food, and to illuminate his dwellings. Later it was put to work burning brush in order to improve the grasslands and to provide ash for fertilizer. From earliest times men considered fire a sacred power. In mythology throughout the world, fire gods abound. In religious ceremonies fire was both feared and worshipped, as in ancient Iran where it was considered a direct incarnation of divinity.

In 1821 an English chemist named John Walker developed the first advance in fire generation since the flint. It was called the ''friction match.'' Made of phosphorous sulphate, it was **46** not too different from the matches used today.

The Grand Canyon

The Grand Canyon in Arizona is the broadest, deepest, and most majestic canyon on earth, its widest areas stretching over 18 miles (30 km) from rim to rim. It was discovered in 1540 by the Spanish explorer Cardenas, who searched for a city of gold and found the Canyon instead. Its stones, he marveled, were "bigger than the great Cathedral Tower of Seville." The Grand Canyon's landscape is characterized by innumerable rock formations that shift in color from one display of reds, pinks, and browns to another as the sun moves across the sky. Its sculptured peaks and buttes stand in stark contrast to the deep, twisting ravines below them. And at the bottom of this 56-mile (90-km) gorge runs the mighty Colorado River.

Geologically the Canyon is an open book depicting a billion years of earth's history. Its rock walls are composed of limestone, sandstone, and shale deposited one layer atop the other. The Colorado River began cutting its way through this great bed of rock about a million years ago, a short span by geological time. This and other erosive action has made the honeycombed, craggy display visitors now behold.

Volcanoes

The volcano is one of the more spectacular and powerful forces in nature. Two thousand years ago Aristotle taught that its action was due to the forces of violent underground winds. Today we know it is an opening in the crust of the earth that allows molten rock, or magma, to escape whenever underground pressures grow too great. This makes the volcano a kind of giant pressure-valve, and it accomplishes in a large way what hot springs, geysers, and fumaroles (small holes for the release of underground gases) do in a lesser capacity.

When a volcano begins to erupt, hot magma forces its way to the surface through a pipelike vent that runs through the center of the volcano. The magma is more than 1,800°F (982°C) when it spews out, but it quickly congeals, turning into flowing black lava. It pours over the edge, building up the crater-topped cones that characterize the world's greatest volcanoes—Mauna Loa in Hawaii, Mt. Vesuvius in Italy, Mt. Fuji in Japan, Mt. Kilimanjaro in Africa.

Volcanic eruptions usually are accompanied by giant clouds, mixtures of carbon dioxide, nitrogen, hydrochloric-acid gas, and sulfur vapor, the latter sometimes giving the cloud a yellowish tint. These clouds can often be enormous. In 1883 when Krakatoa, greatest of all volcanoes, erupted in western Indonesia, dust from its cloud hung in the sky halfway around the world over London for more than two years.

Scientists have been intensively studying the action of volcanoes to discover if signs of coming eruptions can be detected. The consensus is that there are indeed definite warnings. Earthquakes in the vicinity of an active volcano, increased small-scale eruptions, or unusual ground tilts or cracks, all are hints that something far greater is soon to come.

Geysers

A notable feature of Wyoming's Yellowstone National Park is Old Faithful, a geyser that spews its 14,000 gallons (530 dl) of steam and water 150 feet (46 m) high into the air every hour on the hour. Yellowstone Park has, in fact, more geysers than any other spot on earth, almost 200 of them; yet the geyser itself is a relatively rare phenomenon, occurring in other isolated regions throughout Tibet, Central America, Malaysia, Iceland, and New Zealand.

A geyser is usually located in volcanic regions and serves as a sort of subterranean pressure-valve whereby groundwater that has become overheated by neighboring hot lava is allowed to leave the earth through the force of its own expansion. The process begins when the water is transformed into steam by hot rock. The steam expands and forces its way upward through long channels in the earth until it erupts in a spout that can be anything from an inch-high gurgle to a towering jet of steam. Though Old Faithful is the most famous of all such towering jets, the largest is its neighbor, Beehive Geyser. Beehive erupts only on occasion, has been known to **50** send hot steam over 200 feet (70 m) into the air.

Geyser in Yellowstone National Park ▲

Color

The constituents of color perplexed man until the seventeenth century, when it was discovered that each is a component of light. That is, if sunlight passes through a glass prism it becomes a fan-shaped beam divided into seven bands of color: red, orange, yellow, green, blue, indigo, and violet. These colors are inherent though not always visible in white light, and can only be made apparent when they are properly refracted. They cannot be seen at night or on a black surface, which proves that black is the absence of all color. Sir Isaac Newton was the first to note this phenomenon and to develop from it a theory of color. According to Newton, an object has no color of its own but produces color according to the type of light rays it either *absorbs* or *reflects*. Thus, when white light falls on a green leaf, all color rays but green are absorbed into that leaf, while the green rays alone are reflected. An observer looking at the leaf sees only these reflected rays and perceives the leaf as green. This is why objects will not appear in their true colors under artificial light: artificial light does not include the full range of color rays inherent to white light, and thus the type of rays to be reflected or absorbed are limited.

Redwood Trees

Redwood trees are a species of sequoia native to the Pacific Coast of North America. They grow in isolated stands from Monterey, California, to northern Oregon. Preferring a foggy, damp climate, the giant trees thrive in a relatively high terrain, and are rarely found below 3,000 feet (914 m). Redwoods are the largest trees on earth, attaining heights of over 300 feet (91 m), weights of more than 6,000 tons (5,442 M tons), and occasional circumferences of over 100 feet (30 m). They are one of the oldest living things on the planet, sometimes reaching the age of 4,000 years. The reason for the longevity of the redwoods is that the fibrous, reddish brown bark can not only resist the ravaging of insects and fungi but is fireproof as well. These characteristics made it such a popular building material that by the 1930s overzealous logging had "harvested" almost three-quarters of the original 1,500,000 acres (607,500 h) of virgin redwood timber. Today, though man still slowly encroaches on these majestic forests, many of the most spectacular stands are officially protected in state and national parks.

Tundra

Tundra areas are low-lying, barren plains found in the high-latitude areas of Siberia, Europe, and Canada that border the Arctic Ocean. The name tundra comes from the Finnish word *tentur*, which means "marshy plain." To call it "marshy" implies a temperate terrain, however the tundra is an inhospitable and sometimes uninhabitable region characterized by miles of flat, treeless landscape and subzero temperatures.

Though desolate, tundra does possess outstanding natural features. Swamps of bog mosses and lichens nestle in the tundra's rocky valleys, and in areas of Siberian tundra coniferous forests can be found. Numerous lakes, some of haunting beauty, are a familiar sight, as are rushing rivers and unexpected giant outcroppings of rock. During the summer, temperatures in the tundra go as high as 60°F (16°C), promoting the growth of some of the world's most lovely wildflowers. The region is then hospitable for bears and deer, as well as for wild birds that nest in its inaccessible morasses. The arrival of winter quickly hardens the ground, and both animal and man find it a difficult environment for survival.

3 Wonders Of the Animal World

The great number of animal species in this world, their vast variety, difference in size, shape, and habit, are an unceasing wonder to scientists and poets alike. And when we learn of the habits of the individual species—the 2000-mile (3220-km) upstream swim of the salmon to its spawning grounds, the beaver's skill as engineer and architect, the chimpanzee's extraordinary intelligence as problem solver, the lemmings' march of doom to the sea—this amazement is compounded.

The following chapter is a sampling of the diversified creatures that populate our environment. Some are large, some small, but each has a unique characteristic that makes it especially noteworthy.

◄ Honeybees on comb ▲ Sled dogs

▼ Beaver dam ▲ Bald eagle, Alaska

Chimpanzee

The chimpanzee is the best-known and most intelligent anthropoid ape in the family Pongidae. A native of tropical jungles, it is found throughout the rain forests of central and southern Africa, especially between Gambia and the Congo. It lives in small roving bands with a social structure that rivals man's, and subsists mainly on fruits and vegetables.

The chimpanzee measures some five feet tall (1.5 m) and weighs an average of 150 pounds (68 kg). Its arms are longer than its legs and hang below its knees in the characteristic ape posture. Except for its nearly hairless face, the chimp's entire body is covered with thick brown or black hair. Though the brain of a chimpanzee is only half the size of a human's, it still exhibits a degree of reasoning that places it foremost among animal intelligences. Chimps have been trained to count, to work mechanical appliances, and even to communicate with their keepers in a surprisingly sophisticated vocabulary of sounds and gestures. They have a friendly disposition, at least up to the age of two, and show unmistakable signs of both **56** individuality and a sense of humor.

African elephant ▶

Elephant

The largest living land mammal is the elephant, a creature whose size is rivaled only by the great amount of lore surrounding it. In Africa the elephant is worshipped as often as it is hunted. Rumors abound concerning the elephant graveyard, the supposed place where all elephants return to die—and indeed, it is still something of a mystery as to why dead elephants are so rarely found in the jungle.

The elephant is the single survivor of a prehistoric race of pachyderms known as Proboscidea. When full grown it measures ten to fifteen feet (3–4.5 m) in height, the African variety being larger than the Indian, and may weigh 9,000 pounds (4,082 kg). Despite its size it is wonderfully agile in water and remarkably swift on land, as many hunters have learned to their consternation. It is an extremely intelligent animal, living in herds and following a communal life complete with close family system, ''elected'' leaders, and intense group loyalty. Surviving on fruits, tree roots, bark, and tubers, it is one of the longest-lived mammals, having a life span approximately that of a human's. However, the elephant's existence is in danger because of overgrazing and man's hunger for ivory.

Bald Eagle

The United States is but one of the many nations to have used the bald eagle as its national symbol. The ancient Persians had an eagle emblazoned on their spears, as did the Romans. Under Napoleon the eagle became an emblem of the French Republic while the double-headed eagle was long the Austrian coat of arms. The bald eagle (*Haliaetus leucocephalus*) is the most courageous and rapacious of birds. It soars higher and nests higher than practically any flying creature, and will protect its young with ferocity. Though occasionally sighted in Siberia, the bald eagle is found mainly in North America and parts of Europe. It lives on fish it procures in one graceful swooping dive. When food is scarce, however, it will also eat small rodents or carrion. The bald eagle is not really bald at all, contrary to its name, for its head is covered with white downy feathers. Its name derives from its low, flat brow that gives the appearance of being shaved or clipped. Though it is a symbol of the United States and is protected by game laws, this great bird is included on the list of endangered species.

Grizzly Bear

Feared for its ferocity and respected for its intelligence, the great grizzly bear (*Ursus arctos horribilis*) is among the largest and most powerful mammals on earth, standing some nine feet tall (2.7 m) and weighing half a ton. It generally has a tannish brown coat, grizzly or shaggy fur, long, straight claws, and highly developed hind quarters that make it unexpectedly swift and agile. Although it is a carnivore, ordinarily subsisting on fish and small rodents, the grizzly also has a fondness for honey and can survive on berries and vegetables. Unlike others of its species, it is not at all intimidated by man and will attack with little provocation, especially if protecting cubs. At one time the wandering grizzly bear could be found throughout North and Central America. With increased human settlement, however, its territory and food supply were curtailed—a single grizzly will ordinarily hunt in an area as large as 200–300 miles (320–480 km)—and its pelt became sought after by hunters. As a result the grizzly retreated to colder and less accessible parts of North America, where it lives today in ever-dwindling numbers.

Beaver

The beaver, nature's ingenious architect, constructs stick and mud dams along riversides and lakes. These dams, though not always large, can have a profound effect on the environment. Often built at the narrowest point of a stream, they will sometimes back the water up for miles, transforming a swift-flowing current into a placid pond. Bottomland below this point, at the same time, will then tend to drain. Thus, beavers have created many woodland ponds that support lush vegetation and eventually turn into meadowlands. The nests that cause these alterations are dome-shaped and are reinforced with stones and mud, the mud being layered on by the beaver and then smoothed over by its tail, which the beaver uses like a trowel. Within this compact home dwell one or two beaver families.

However, there is little social contact among beavers and they work independently. During the winter they retreat to the parts of their homes that are beneath the ice and subsist there on roots, water plants, and bark that they have stored during the warmer months. The beaver is an aquatic animal, equipped with webbed feet, a sleek, water-repellent coat, and a broad tail that it uses as a rudder while swimming (the beaver also uses its tail to alert its companions of an intruder by loudly slapping the water with it). In the nineteenth century its·pelt was a prize among trappers, sold both for dress trimmings and for a type of man's hat known as a "beaver." Today, beaver hunting has been curtailed as their importance in maintaining the natural environment has finally been realized.

Locust

Although the term "locust" popularly describes a wide range of migratory grasshoppers, the true locust is a species known as *Locusta migratoria*, one of the most destructive insects known to the world. Traveling in swarms of immeasurable size and density that sometimes literally darken the sky, they indicate their approach by a peculiar buzzing that since Biblical days has been a warning of disaster. A swarm can denude areas of vegetation in a short time, moving methodically from field to field until practically every growing thing is devoured. Outbreaks usually take place in warm, dry grasslands or at the borders of deserts. Swarms have been recorded in the midwestern United States, throughout the desert regions of Asia and Australia, and in the central grasslands of Africa. Though certain insecticides are effective against their onslaught, and though the locust does have a number of natural predators, the great size of their hordes plus their unpredictable schedules (locusts appear and disappear throughout the years in no recognizable patterns) indicate that they have by no means been eradicated from the world today.

Dolphin

No aquatic animal has more rapport with man than the dolphin. Tested endlessly in the laboratory, dolphins have been trained to perform the most sophisticated maneuvers, and have been been taught to communicate with man by means of a special language. Many myths center on this wonderful creature: The Greeks deemed it sacred and made it the mount of ocean divinities. Dionysus once turned a whole boatload of pirates into dolphins. Mariners told of how drowning men would be rescued by these animals or of how a dolphin following a ship was a sure sign of fair weather to come. Even today these sleek seagoers have been known to frolic with children in shallow inland waters.

A member of the whale family, the dolphin communicates with its kind using a type of sonar. The dolphin's head is long, with a tapered snout that holds some 200 teeth. Over its eyes is a semilunar blowhole through which it breathes (like all whales, the dolphin is a mammal). Being a gregarious creature, the dolphin swims in a pack. It is extremely solicitous of its young, which it bears in litters of one or two, and which it affectionately suckles for many months after birth.

63

▲ Bottle-nosed dolphin

Condor

The condor is one of the largest of birds—its wing spread can exceed ten feet (3 m)—and is one of the longest lived, sometimes attaining 60 years of age. It is a native of the mountains, found in the Andes and in the California Sierras, where it soars to elevations of 15,000 feet (4,570 m) along the thermal currents of the earth. Unlike its relative the eagle, the condor builds no nest but lays its eggs on bare rocks. The rarest member of this already rare species is the Californian Condor. This bird has a black body with white linings on its wings, a yellow head, powerful talons, plus the flattened brow and hooked neck of its South American counterpart. Like the Andean Condor, it is a nocturnal creature, able to see vast distances in the black of the night, and similarly lives on a diet of carrion. When especially hungry it is not above attacking live sheep, goats, and even deer, which it does by swooping down and inflicting lethal wounds with its sharp, hooked beak. Due to their dwindling numbers, Californian Condors are protected by strict game laws; only 40 or 50 of them are believed to remain, most in the area around Santa Barbara, California.

▲ Andean Condor

Wolf

Though the wolf is a relative of the dog and is thought to be its progenitor, it is a far more powerful creature and displays certain behavioral habits diametrically opposed to those of its domesticated relation. While a dog pays allegiance to man, a wolf is fiercely loyal to its pack. At the head of this pack is a male chieftain who receives absolute obedience from all members and who will lose authority only when defeated by a more powerful competitor. Below him a pecking order extends, the arrangement determined both by hunting prowess—wolves always hunt in packs—and ability in battle. The females of the species, meanwhile, are chosen through combat among the males. Once the choices have been made mates will remain together for life, rearing their young with great affection and maintaining a strong nuclear family.

Wolves are carnivorous beasts, pursuing their prey, both domestic and wild, with such intelligent stratagems that they have traditionally been the bane of sheperds and hunters alike. As a result the wolf population has slowly been decreasing. Packs can still be found in the southeastern and southwestern United States, northern Canada, and Siberia.

65

▲ Timber wolves

Butterfly

There are more than 100,000 species of butterflies and moths, many of which are noteworthy for their elaborately colorful wing markings. Of all insects, it is probably these that we most admire, not only because of their beauty but their dramatic transformation from caterpillar to butterfly. This process takes place in three stages: The first begins when the larva is hatched from the egg and emerges in the familiar shape of the caterpillar. For varying periods of time it remains in this state, devouring leaves and greenery with an appetite that occasionally turns it into an agricultural pest. Next it enters the pupa or chrysalis stage in which, usually using a silken substance secreted from its own body (it is this substance which is extracted from the silkworm and spun into silk) it weaves its cocoon. It remains enclosed within this tight nest from several weeks to half a year. Finally it cuts its way through the hard skin of the cocoon, hangs upside-down for several hours to allow the blood to fill its wingpads, and then flies into the summer winds. Depending on its species, it lives from periods of several days to several months.

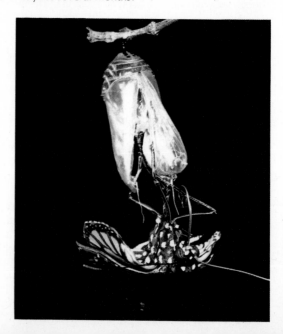

Honeybee

The honeybee is among the most interesting of all communal creatures. It is valuable for its honey and wax but more important for its pollination of plants. Within the beehive there are three types of bees: the workers, the drones, and the queen. Unlike anthills, where the workers are neuter and the males do much of the work, in beehives all workers are sterile females and the male drones exist only to fertilize the queen. Worker bees each have a particular function that they will automatically perform just hours after birth. This they will follow with absolute dedication all their lives. They will even sacrifice themselves to sting in defense of the hive. Aside from those who gather pollen and nectar and make honey, there are nurses, maids, guards, and even undertakers.

The queen is the center of the hive and lives longer than all the other bees, sometimes for several years. She can be distinguished from the rest of the bees by her large abdomen. She is fertilized only once during her life by a drone. After this "maiden flight" she returns to her hive, never to leave again. **67**

◀ Monarch butterfly emerging from cocoon

Whale

The whale is not a fish but a mammal, the largest the world has known. Certain types of blue whales, for example, reach a length of 100 feet (30 m) and weigh as much as 150 tons (136 M tons), dwarfing the elephant and even exceeding in bulk the largest dinosaurs. In past centuries the whale has been hunted by man with such vengeance that many varieties are approaching disappearance. The problem is that the whale is valuable for so many people: the Eskimos utilize its blubber and cook its meat; whale oil still lights lamps around the world; ambergris, a waxy secretion of the sperm whale, is an essential ingredient in the best perfumes; and even the bones of the whale have been carved by sailors for generations, their engravings known as "scrimshaw."

Basically there are two kinds of whales. The *Mysticeti* includes so-called whalebone whales. Instead of teeth they have a horny triangular plate, called a baleen, that serves as a sieve in separating the whale's food from the water. The second kind is the *Odontoceti,* or the toothed whales, which include the bottle-nosed and sperm whales. Dolphins and porpoises are also whales, members of the toothed family.

▲ Killer whale

Horse

The horse in its natural state belongs to a herd which thousands of years ago could be found running free throughout Europe and Asia. After its domestication in the fifth millennium B.C. it became an emblem of authority (the equestrian statue was always a symbol of royalty) and of power (conquering nations such as the Hittites, the Persians, and later the Greeks and Romans were all based on strong cavalry and chariot enforcements). The horse also provided, it was discovered, superior recreation: horseraces were run in China as early as 1000 B.C. and in Greece during the Olympic Games.

Characterized by its size and strength, its intelligence (ranked just below the ape, dog, and elephant), and its responsiveness to man, the horse makes an excellent beast of burden and a dependable mount. Being of such importance, it played a large part in diverse religions—from Hinduism to Egyptian and Greek mythology. In the American West, the cowboy and his faithful steed have become a special part of the folklore. **69**

▲ Polo ponies

Ant

The 10,000 known ant species have amazing diversity and distribution. They are the most successful of communal insects. Almost all build elaborately engineered nests. Within these nests are labyrinthine corridors that connect one chamber to another, some of which are used for hatch eggs, some for storing food, and some for general living space.

An ant colony begins with a winged queen who mates while in flight with a single male. After this mating flight the male is left to die along with a number of other unsuccessful suitors. The queen founds her colony by immediately laying thousands of eggs. Soon the eggs hatch and the colony grows, and barring outside disruption, it prospers for the queen's lifetime, which can be as long as 15 years. Within the nest there are three kinds of ants: queen, male, and worker, the last being of neuter gender. The workers include giant soldier ants, who police the colony and crush all invaders with their huge mandibles; smaller workers, who forage for food; and domestic ants, who remain within the hill, tending the young and making repairs on the nest.

Salmon

The two features that make the salmon remarkable are its mating habits and the fact that certain species are "anadromous," that is, able to live in both fresh and salt water. Every autumn this creature leaves its home in the sea and begins a long, heroic migration swim up one of the continental rivers, pushing against the current in an attempt to reach the spot where it was hatched. So great is its migratory instinct that it will brave uphill water courses, a host of natural predators, whitewater narrows, and even waterfalls on its journey. This it does by leaping over all obstacles—some species are able to go as high as 15 feet (4.5 m) into the air—or by cleverly ferreting out alternate routes when impediments are too great. The distances covered by salmon are sometimes enormous. Every year the king salmon must swim more than 2,000 miles up the Yukon River before it can finally spawn in its native headwaters.

Dog

Of all creatures in the animal kingdom none is so faithful or loyal to man as the dog. Though the dog is a member of a family of quadrupeds that includes the fox, wolf, and jackal, it among all its cousins is the only creature to maintain unswerving allegiance to man. This has long puzzled zoologists, and many of their theories center on the fact that the dog, being a pack animal and accustomed to following a single leader, has transferred its loyalty from an animal leader to a human one, and maintained this bond.

Though all domesticated dogs belong to one species, *Canis familiaris,* it is difficult to believe they are all related when looking at the wide variety of breeds. Between the largest of these, the St. Bernard, which reaches weights of 250 pounds (113 kg), and the smallest, the Chihuahua, standing six inches high (15 cm), the difference is astonishing. Evidence indicates that the dog was first domesticated in Asia some 14,000 years ago when it strayed near man's fires. Today it is still valuable as a watchdog, hunter, guide, herder, sled bearer, and probably most important, as a companion.

Lemming

One of the most peculiar and mysterious of creatures is the lemming. The peculiarity of this animal does not stem from its appearance, however, nor from its day-to-day living habits. Looking much like a common hamster, it is small, some five to seven inches (13–18 cm) long, and has grayish brown fur. It is found in the far northern areas of Europe and North America. What sets it off from other animals is that for reasons no one understands, during certain periods of the year each lemming begins a frantic dash across country, devouring everything in its track and devastating vegetable life. This obsessive march continues, if it is not killed along the way, until the lemming eventually arrives at the sea, at which point it leaps madly into the water and continues to swim till it sinks from exhaustion. There are several explanations of this strange phenomenon. Some believe it is the lemming's natural method of population control—and indeed it is one of the few animals to breed all year round. Others claim the marches are a response to food shortages, and still others claim stress and overcrowding within lemming packs cause this behavior.

◀ Sled dogs

4 Wonders of Mankind: Monuments

Throughout history man has responded to his environment by trying to imitate and interpret it, and by undertaking to improve it. The impulse to improve has generated our scientific disciplines and all the wonders created through them that are part of modern life: the radio, telephone, airplane, and many more. Imitation and interpretation have produced art, and from it stems the great monuments designed and erected by human genius. In this chapter we will see man's passion and skill at fashioning the inspiring landmarks that have characterized his culture and art for centuries.

▲ Cathedral in Orvieto, Italy ▼ Machu Picchu, Peru ▲ Buddhas, Angkor Wat

Stonehenge

The monument of Stonehenge is an extensive grouping of massive stones standing like solitary sentries on Salisbury Plain, England. There is great mystery surrounding this collection of megaliths. Some claim Stonehenge is simply an ancient Druid sanctuary. Others maintain it is an antique observatory; and indeed, certain stones line up in meaningful patterns during the solstices while others mark significant risings and settings of the sun. Construction on Stonehenge began around 2400 B.C., and was built in several stages. It consists of a central stone—the altar—surrounded by two circles of stones. Two rings of pits surround these and further out is another pit ring. The entire complex is then enclosed by a circular ditch with an entranceway facing the northwest. The size of the stones are awesome, some weighing 50 tons (45 M tons) and standing 21 feet (6.3 m) tall. How they were transported to this site is unknown. Legend says that Merlin the magician floated them through the air from Ireland; and strangely the type of bluestone of which the megaliths are composed is found only in Ireland and parts of Wales, ancient centers of Druid culture.

The Louvre

Everyone knows the Louvre as perhaps the greatest art museum in the world; few know it as a royal residence. Yet to the literate Frenchman, it is still the *Palais du Louvre*—the Louvre Palace. One has to go back nearly 800 years to find a Paris without a Louvre. In 1190 a cylindrical tower was built near the Seine to house the royal treasury and King Philip's hunting dogs (*Louveterie* is from the Latin *lupara*, meaning a kennel of wolfhounds.) The castle was soon razed, and for seven centuries a parade of kings and queens built on its foundations. Charles V made the Louvre the official royal residence, adding walls, smaller towers, even a library, while Francis I filled it with art masterpieces. With the architect l'Orme, Catherine de Medici continued its enlargement, and by 1610 Henri IV had made it the grandest palace in Europe. One of Henri's magnificent improvements was the Grande Galerie, a corridor so long that he and his entourage would sometimes stage fox hunts inside it. Louis XIV, born in the Louvre, neglected it all his life, though his son and grandson filled it with their art treasures. By the mid-nineteenth century it was finally declared a national museum. **77**

Chichén Itzá

Much of what we know today about the Mayan Indians has come from excavations at Chichén Itzá, a ruined city of the Yucatán peninsula in Mexico. Founded in 530 A.D., Chichén Itzá was at first only an outpost of Mayan society and was soon abandoned. Then the gods, legend tells, guided priests of the Itzá tribe back to this spot in 965 where they resettled and rebuilt. For the next five centuries, until its sudden and inexplicable abandonment in the fifteenth century, it would be the heart of Mayan civilization.

Like all ancient civilizations, religion inspired Mayan social and architectural concerns. In the center of the city is the Temple of the Thousand Columns, a plaza with shrines pyramids, courts, gardens, and even an open-air theatre. Near it is the famous observatory of El Caraco, the "snail," so-called because of its great domed roof. Mayan priests made the astronomical calculations in this building that led to the development of their sophisticated calendar and knowledge of eclipses. In Chichén Itzá there is also a "ball-court," where a peculiar ritual game was played using a rubber ball that was hit by the body. In the heart of the city is the Castillo, a stepped, four-sided pyramid that reaches a hundred feet (30 m) at the pinnacle and spreads to an acre at the base. Quetzalcoatl, chief god of the Mayan pantheon, was worshipped here in the form of a feathered serpent. Here, too, human sacrifice was offered to the deity's omnivorous appetite and to the thousands of observers who witnessed the event.

▲ Temple of the Thousand Columns

▲ Castillo ▼ Observatory

Santa Sophia

In the year 530 A.D. Justinian, Emperor of Byzantium, leveled many acres in the city of Constantinople (now Istanbul) and commandeered the services of 16,000 of its best artisans, all for a magnificent whim: he wished to build the most beautiful Christian church in the world. This work was seven years in the making. Justinian financed it by expropriating the salaries of his state officials, closing the schools, and forcing his army to labor without pay. Santa Sophia's central feature is its great dome. The subsidiary architectural supports include a new invention, the pendentive, a triangular piece of corner vaulting that allows a round dome to rest on a square base. The plan of the church is basically a square, though this is difficult to discern through the building's maze of galleries, colonnades, turrets, carved cornices, and many-shaped windows. The interior has a high-walled central chamber where mosaics depicting Christian themes were once displayed. The mosaics were removed, however, in the year 1453 when Constantinople was conquered by the Moslem Turks. Santa Sophia the cathedral was turned into Hagia Sophia the mosque, and has since become a museum of Byzantine art.

Interior cupola ▶

Dome of the Rock

The oldest of all mosques is the Dome of the Rock, built in Jerusalem in 691 A.D. by the caliph Abd-al-Malik. After the Kaaba stone in Mecca it is the most revered Moslem sanctuary in the world. The Dome is centered on a great square that covers a large portion of the entire city, and is said to rest on the ruins of Solomon's temple. The central feature of its interior is a large outcropping of granite some 60 feet (18 m) long that some consider to be the center of the world. Upon this stone Abraham is said to have prepared to sacrifice Isaac, and Moslems believe that Muhammad was once transported here from Mecca by a winged horse and that the animal's footprints still remain embedded in the stone. On this very spot, too, Christians believe that Christ once preached a sermon.

Today the Dome of the Rock is remarkably well preserved considering its age. It has an eight-sided base crowned by a wooden dome that in turn rests on a high drum displaying 16 windows in its circumference. The exterior of the building is covered with exquisite mosaics and calligraphic verses from the Koran. The sanctuary is reached by several marble staircases, and its courtyards are regularly filled with worshipers.

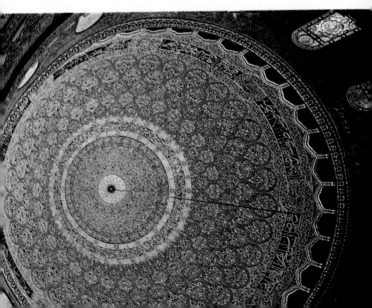

Shwe Dagon

The pagoda of Shwe Dagon is said to have been built during the time of Buddha, though its present structure dates from the fifteenth to eighteenth century. In order to understand this most important Buddhist shrine in Rangoon, Burma, one must know of the prototype on which it is modeled, the "stupa." The stupa is a conical tower divided into sections, each symbolizing an aspect of the relationship between heaven and earth and between the spirit and the body. Originally built as a mound over graves of saints, the stupa evolved through the ages into a sacred emblem unto itself.

Shwe Dagon is the most imposing stupa in the city, some would say in the world. Its design is essentially a single tower surrounded by many smaller towers in the stupa form, all surrounded by shrines and countless images of Buddha. The central tower, built of brick, rises to a height of 358 feet (112 m). It can be seen for miles around as a reminder of the relics buried beneath it: eight hairs from the body of Buddha. So sacred is Shwe Dagon to the Burmese that today it is a common sight to see even important government officials sweeping its walkways as an act of religious devotion.

The Châteaux of France

The châteaux lining the Loire Valley of France represent the transition between the Gothic style and that of the Renaissance, an example of how the art of two nations, France and Italy, can combine to form a unique third style. There are two kinds of châteaux in France: the *château fort,* or fortified palace; and the *château de plaisance,* the palace of pleasure. The first, dating mainly from the fifteenth century, are bastions of defense as much as they are family residences. A famous example is Longeais, built in 1465, its entrance marked by three towers with battlements and conical roofs joined by a causeway for defense. Walls and battlements, however, soon became outmoded. Whenever a château was planned in the sixteenth century it was planned for pleasure and beauty. Defense was left up to the large armies of mercenary soldiers usually garrisoned nearby.

Not only royalty built châteaux in France but members of a newly emerging power group, the *bourgeoisie,* did as well. **84** Chenonceaux, for example, was the work of Thomas Bohier, a

Azay-le-Rideau ▲

nouveau riche merchant. Started in 1515, its Gothic towers combined with classic friezes and Renaissance walkways, a perfect transitional structure. Amboise, erected like many other châteaux on the remains of a medieval fortress, dates from between 1470 to 1495. Its designer, Charles VIII, traveled to Italy while the building was in construction and upon returning ordered that Italianate loggias, arcades, and gardens be added to the already existing Gothic façade. It was at Amboise that several hundred Protestant leaders were put to death by Catherine de Medici, and here too the body of Leonardo da Vinci is said to lie. Azay-le-Rideau is another amalgam of two styles, built in 1518 by the finance minister of Louis XII. Though fortifications were no longer necessary, Azay rests on pilings set into the river Indre, providing it with a kind of natural moat. It has a steeply pitched Gothic roof and circular towers at each of its four corners, is faced with white limestone, and ornamented with classical relief sculpture. It is perhaps the most typical of all French châteaux, and some say the most perfect as well. **85**

▲ Château in Normandy

Hoover Dam

In its time Hoover Dam (originally Boulder Dam) was the greatest engineering feat ever attempted, designed with bulwarks 300 feet (91 m) higher than those of any other dam on earth. Its purpose was to block up the rushing Colorado River, thus creating a 115 mile- (185 km-) long reservoir known as Lake Mead. Initiated in 1914, over 13 years were spent simply surveying the site. When actual construction began in 1930 it involved 5,000 workers as well as seven million tons of cement, more concentrated weight than had ever before been placed on the planet by man. Work continued for six years. The completed project looms 726 feet (217 m) high, spans 1,244 feet (363 m) across, and is thicker at the base than a city block. Today it still serves many functions including conservation, recreation, protection from floods, power generation, and of course provision of water for areas of the Southwest that would otherwise be uninhabitable.

The Parthenon

High on a hill in the center of Athens, Greece, sits the Parthenon, the most splendid temple in that complex of ancient sanctuaries known as the Acropolis. The building was dedicated to Pallas Athena, goddess of wisdom, and was designed by the architects Ictinus and Callicrates under the overseership of the greatest of Greek sculptors, Phidias. Construction on the building began in 447 B.C. and took nine years to complete, much of the time being spent in excavating a 40-foot (12-m) cellar beneath the temple through solid rock. The building was rectangular, each side decorated with rows of colonnades. It measured 228 feet (60 m) long, and 101 feet (30 m) wide.

From the time of its construction to the fifth century A.D. the Parthenon remained intact. Then conquering Christians replaced the statue of Athena with one of the Holy Virgin. Through the following centuries the monument would be used as a church, a mosque, a powder magazine, and even as a target for artillery practice. In modern times, after the building had been half shot away and the best of its sculpted figures removed to the British Museum, recognition finally came, and today it is one of the world's most famous landmarks. **87**

The Palace of Versailles

The Palace of Versailles was built because Louis XIV hated Paris. Born and brought up in this capital city of France, he had passed a harsh childhood here and always recalled these days with bitterness. Upon ascending the throne he decided to move his court out of the despised city, choosing for new quarters the small country town of Versailles. He ordered a palace built here, the grandest ever seen in the West.

In 1661 Louis commissioned the architects Le Vau and Mansard to oversee Versailles, and work on it continued to 1708, most of the labor being carried on during the first 20 years. However, before half the structure was up Louis was moving his court into residence. For 50 years he remained here, watching over every detail of social and political life.

Through the years the palace underwent a number of additions and modifications, though the integrity of Louis' plans were always respected. Today the building is approached by **88** three main roads leading to an enormous courtyard and to a

central palace that is flanked on either side by two attached wings. Surrounding the main building are miles of park still meticulously kept. Features of this great monument include the famous Hall of Mirrors, a corridor 235 feet (70 m) long lined with mirrors and with murals painted by the great Le Brun. Here Louis once greeted the Siamese ambassador wearing an ermine coat so heavily encrusted with diamonds that a servant had to support him. The grounds of the palace include a greenhouse called the Orangerie where tropical fruits were cultivated especially for the King's table. Also, there were man-made canals for gondolas from Venice, several artificial lakes, miles of woods stocked with game for the royal hunt, statuary by Europe's best sculptors, waterfalls, grottoes, and two small palaces, the Grand and Petit Trianon. The latter was fittingly dedicated to the god of love; for it was here that Marie Antoinette and her gay entourage frolicked away their days in romantic fantasies even as the very eve of the French Revolution drew near. **89**

Mont-Saint-Michel

The hill on which the noted abbey of Mont-Saint-Michel rests has always been a sacred place. Once a pagan shrine, the Romans replaced it with a temple to Jupiter, and the Christians in turn razed it in favor of a small chapel. All during this time the hill was surrounded by farmland and small villages. In 725, however, an earthquake caused the ocean to swallow up the land at the base of the shrine, turning the hill into an island a half-mile out to sea. Mont-Saint-Michel was not totally cut off, however: twice a day the tide, one of the highest in the world, rolled out to sea, leaving the hillock briefly connected to the mainland by a stretch of white beach. The monks who lived through this quake took their survival as a divine omen and built a monastic community on the newly formed island. A thriving town soon arose, in the middle of which stood a series of chapels and a main abbey, its tower crowned by a statue of St. Michael. Over the years the town prospered and was besieged by many invaders; but always the inexorable tides discouraged their schemes. Today, however, a causeway links the isle to the land, allowing visitors to go as they please.

The Eiffel Tower

Alexandre Gustave Eiffel was a respectable but little-known French bridge-builder who became world-famous as the engineer and designer of France's most famous modern monument, the Eiffel Tower. Eiffel designed this structure for the Paris Exposition of 1889. When completed, an elevator took passengers up an interlaced iron tower that measured 984 feet (295 m) high and weighed 7,000 tons (6,350 M tons) in steel alone. It was not simply its monumentality that stunned the world, however, but the fact that for the first time the unlimited possibilities of iron girder construction were demonstrated. Previously architects had been timid concerning the use of the laced-girder principle, and had no notion of how much weight buildings of this type might support. Eiffel's creation was thus a sudden leap forward, and its vertical-diagonal bracing design became a prototype for many of the skyscrapers that followed. It was not until 1930 when the Empire State Building was raised in New York that its towers were over-reached.

The Statue of Buddha in Bamiyan Valley

High in the Hindu Kush Mountains of Afghanistan stands the second largest statue on earth (the first is the statue of ''Motherland'' near Volgograd, U.S.S.R.). Though practically unknown beyond a small circle of art historians, this figure, a giant rock image of Buddha towering 175 feet (53 m), is so momentous that its huge foot is taller than a man. The figure, carved in the third century A.D., is fitted into a niche along a limestone cliff that runs the length of the narrow Bamiyan Valley. The monument's heavy proportions, its rigid frontal position, and the symmetrical folds of its cloak mark it as an example of late Gandhara art, a style that combined the Greco-Roman classicism brought by Mediterranean silk merchants with indige-

92

nous Eastern motifs. Originally the body of the Buddha figure was covered with gold leaf and the niche was decorated with mosaics, though today the leaf has vanished and only fragments of the paintings remain. The colossal statue, moreover, was just part of a complex of monastic caves, grottoes, and sanctuaries built from the fourth to the sixth centuries by the 1,500 Buddhist monks inhabiting the valley. This great center of religion and learning was destroyed in the tenth century by conquering Moslems who not only annihilated the entire Buddhist community but defaced its art as well, destroying the statue's face and hands (the word "deface" originates from the Moslem practice of smashing the face and limbs of statuary) and leaving the damaged remains we see today.

The Leaning Tower of Pisa

The Italian city of Pisa lies 44 miles (71 km) west of Florence. Once a city of enormous wealth, it is still noteworthy for its architectural monuments, among them an eleventh-century cathedral, ancient Roman baths, and most famous, the "Leaning Tower." The latter, started in 1174 and completed in the fourteenth century, is believed to be the design of well-known Pisan architect Bonanno Pisano. Originally erected as a bell tower, it is a lovely example of Italian architecture in its own right, tubular in shape, with eight stories reaching to a height of 184 feet (55 m), walls 13 feet (4 m) thick, a winding stairway inside, and picturesque marble inlays throughout. What characterizes this building as a true wonder is its surprising and almost comical tilt. Due to repeated geological tremors in the area, this tilt was already well established by the time of Galileo, who is said to have dropped weights off the top to ascertain the velocity of falling objects. In the 1700s the building had moved almost 16 feet (5 m) out of plumb, and by the next century had shifted another 2 feet (.6 m). If the foundations had not been reinforced in the twentieth century, the lean in the Leaning Tower would have caused its doom.

The Colosseum

Though the Colosseum was not the largest amphitheater in ancient Rome it is today by far the most famous, perhaps because it was here that the martyrdom of the Christian faithful occurred. The Colosseum itself was constructed in the form of a giant ellipse some 612 feet long (183 m), 515 feet across (154 m), and 160 feet high (48m). Surrounded by a row of pilasters, it had 80 doorways on the ground story over which were erected three tiers. Construction was initiated by the Emperor Vespasian and completed by Titus in 80 A.D. who celebrated its opening by games lasting 100 days during which time 5,000 wild animals were slaughtered.

The Christians were but one of several sacrifices offered at the Colosseum, all for the entertainment of emperor and citizens. The arena was at times filled with gladiators that battled not only with one another but against lions, bulls, bears, and other savage animals. Criminals were tortured and duels fought, but perhaps the greatest spectacle was when the bottom of the amphitheater was flooded and actual sea battles were enacted, complete with Roman galleys and a thousand fighting men.

Angkor Wat

The greatest civilization ever known in Cambodia was during the Middle Ages under the Khmer kings. The glory of their reign was reflected in Angkor Wat, a monumental structure combining the function of monastery, fortress, and temple with that of royal residence. This was not an unusual practice, for the king of Cambodia was believed to be a divine incarnation of the Hindu god Vishnu and hence his palace was a heaven on earth (the name Angkor Wat means "Palace Monastery"). Angkor Wat was started in 1112 A.D. by King Suryaraman and was completed by his nephew 68 years later. One of the largest temples on earth, the square moat surround-

total length. In approaching the building one follows a long, straight walkway leading through a series of square enclosing walls up to the main building constructed on a quadrangular base. The temple has four conical towers at each corner and one in the center, all of them honeycombed with carvings of Vishnu in his paradise. Noteworthy also are the huge carved heads situated at various places in the temple and the bas-relief sculpture that displays graceful dancing figures, scenes of war, world creation, processions, and groups of tableaus taken from the Hindu epic, the *Mahabharata*. Later, when Cambodia became a Buddhist country, statues of Buddhist deities were added to the Hindu designs, thus making the building sacred to both religions, as it is still today.

St. Peter's Church

The Church of St. Peter in Rome sits at the entranceway to that theocratic metropolis, Vatican City, one of the many buildings comprising the world headquarters of the Catholic Church. It is built on the site of a far older cathedral, a basilica erected by Constantine the Great in 306 A.D. This monument was in turn constructed on an early Christian necropolis, the supposed burial ground of St. Peter. (In the early 1940s Vatican excavators digging beneath the altar claimed to have discovered the very bones of the apostle himself.) Through the centuries Constantine's basilica was pillaged, rebuilt, and finally allowed to fall into ruin. In 1450 Pope Nicholas V, fearing the church's loss of temporal power, decreed that the old church be razed and a greater one placed in its spot as symbol of the church triumphant. Fifty-six years later Pope Julius II began work on the project. The original ground plan was a Greek cross as designed by the great Bramante. This blueprint was scrapped at the designer's death by other architects (including Raphael), and for more than 30 years incessant modifications and at times entire reconstructions were imposed upon the building while in construction. In 1546 Pope Paul III called in the 72-year-old Michelangelo, commissioning him to design the dome, an architectural feat fraught with problems due to the large distance to be spanned. The great Florentine solved the problem by forming the dome of two concentric shells and supporting it with spokelike stone ribs.

The nave of St. Peter's was completed in 1612, the facade and portico two years later. In length the church was 613 feet (187 m), in breadth 445 feet (133 m). Inside are decorated pillars, mosaic floors, great lacunar ceilings, a magnificent golden altar, and statues by the finest sculptors including Michelangelo, Bernini, and later Canova. It was dedicated by Pope Urban VIII more than a hundred years after the first stones had been laid. It is now the largest church in Christendom, and the highest domed building in the world.

Persepolis

Persepolis, a city of ancient Persia located some 35 miles (56 km) northwest of Shiraz, Iran, is perhaps the archetypical ruined city of antiquity. Four hundred years B.C., Persepolis was the most powerful and wealthy city in the Middle East, capital of the Achaemenian kings among whose ranks were Darius and Cyrus the Great. Its ruins indicate that the entire city was built above the desert on a raised terrace bounded on three sides by a single great wall. The 13 enormous columns remaining in the Audience Hall of Darius are the tallest in antiquity and show this to have been the largest building of its time. Other remains include marble stairways, walls and door arches, and various inscriptions, including the famous petition of Darius: "God protect this country from foe, famine and falsehood." There is also a series of bas-reliefs that depict hunting and religious scenes. All of this was brought to the ground in 331 B.C. It was then that Alexander the Great, making his way across the world, destroyed Persepolis to demonstrate to potential foes the extent of his military might.

Borobudur

Though today Buddhism has long disappeared from Java, many of its monuments remain, reminders that during the first ten centuries A.D. Malaysia was predominantly under the sway of Indian culture. In Java, Buddhism's greatest flower was the temple of Borobudur, built in the eighth and ninth centuries by the Sailendra princes. The name Borobudur means "many buddhas," and the temple is worthy of its name. Its shape is that of a truncated pyramid, the top platform displaying a large central stupa (see page 82 for explanation of stupa) encircled by 72 smaller ones. On the sides of the pyramid rise a series of stepped terraces, each accessible by a central staircase. These terraces are filled with statuary and bas-relief depicting scenes from the life of Buddha, the lower terraces showing his earthly travails, the higher ones his divine enlightenment. The ninth century pilgrim (more than 10,000 visited this sanctuary in a single month) walked through the ascending terraces in a prescribed path witnessing on its walls a religious drama that chronicled the soul's ascent from the physical world to the spiritual, thus receiving a lesson in metaphysics as well as esthetics.

The Alhambra

In the year 1238 A.D. the caliph Al Ahmar initiated the building of a citadel in the town of Granada, located in the foothills of southern Spain. Construction on the project went on for over a century and was finally completed in 1358. The finished structure was a combination royal office, fortress, and pleasure ground. It consisted of a large castle built in classic Moorish style, a palace with many smaller residential suites attached to it, a thick turreted wall, courtyards, and magnificent gardens that included waterfalls, fountains, and wall mosaics depicting ornamental arabesques intertwined with verses from the Koran. An Arab poet was inspired to call this grand work "a pearl set around with emeralds."

Though the Alhambra was to be the bastion of Islam in Europe for a thousand years, the Moors occupied it scarcely a hundred before they were expelled from Spain by Christian conquerors in 1492. Charles V rebuilt part of the main palace in the sixteenth century, tearing down one of its most splendid sections to replace it with an ordinary Italian-style palazzo. In 1812 a main tower was destroyed and nine years later an earthquake did further damage. In the last century however, much of the building was restored, and today it stands as the **102** most characteristic piece of Moorish architecture in Europe.

Mecca

The spiritual center of the Moslem religion is the city of Mecca, in Saudi Arabia. In the year 630 A.D. Muhammad marched into Mecca with an army of 10,000 men and decreed it the sacred center of Islam. Mecca was his birthplace and contained the *kaaba*, a 40-foot-high (12m) cubical stone long worshipped in pre-Islamic Arabia and said to have been built by Abraham on God's command. Thereafter, the faithful recited prayers five times a day facing its direction, and all mosques were built on an axis similarly aligned. Today the *kaaba*, object of 200,000 yearly pilgrimages, sits within a magnificent open structure called the Great Mosque. A pilgrim arriving in the holy city goes directly to this shrine where he kisses the sacred "black stone" set into the eastern wall of the *kaaba*, then perambulates the sanctuary seven times reciting appropriate prayers. This pilgrimage is a Moslem obligation, and it is occasionally made under remarkably severe conditions—there are records of pilgrims crawling all the way to Mecca or walking the entire distance backwards. When the trip is completed the pilgrim is honored in his community and his name dignified with a special title: *Hadji,* or "one who has made the journey."

104

The *Kaaba* ▲

Easter Island

Easter Island, a tiny volcanic spot of land 2,000 miles (3,200 km) off Chile, is the home of those most imposing monuments, the now famous *aku* figures, some of which tower 20 feet high (6 m) and weigh 50 tons (45.3 M tons). Most of these face the sea on burial platforms known as *ahu;* others stand alone. All, however, have been a mystery since they were first discovered on Easter Day, 1722, by a Dutch sea captain, Jacob Roggeveen. Were they images to ancestral spirits or statues of gods? Why are they all identical, each with tapered head, turned-up nose, long ears, and high, almost Mongolian-like cheekbones? When were they carved? And the greatest enigma, how were they dragged into place? At no time has the population of Easter Island exceeded 4,000 inhabitants. Yet with stone chisels alone many hundreds of these megaliths were carved from volcanic rock, then transported from quarry to site many miles away, a job that would ordinarily require an army of laborers. There is one other puzzle: some statues are left unfinished or lie abandoned halfway between quarry and site. For some unknown reason work on the statues ceased and was never resumed.

The Great Wall of China

From the Gulf of the Yellow Sea in the east to the western borders of Inner Mongolia winds 1,500 miles (2,400 km) of the most ambitious construction project of all time, the Great Wall of China. What its original purpose was is not thoroughly understood, though it was probably both a boundary marker (still today it divides the northern grazing lands from the southern farm country) and a fortification against raids from Tartar marauders. The Wall is built of brick, rising from a granite foundation 40 feet high (12 m), on top of which is a walkway measuring 15 feet (4.5 m) across. At intervals of 200 yards (180 m) block towers are stationed; in each a sentry was once posted, sometimes for the duration of his entire life. The Great Wall was completed in the third century B.C. by Emperor Shih Huang Ti, who employed more than a million men to connect several existing walls into one continuous chain. Intensive work lasted only about 20 years, though modifications went on for centuries. Thousands of laborers perished on the job and were enterred within the wall as construction continued thus making it the world's largest necropolis as well as the longest fortification.

The Ajanta Caves

In the early centuries A.D. Buddhists were often persecuted in India. So, like the early Christians that fled to the catacombs, many of the Buddhist devout took to the underground. The result was that much of the best Buddhist art in India is cave art, with some of the finest examples being the frescoes from the Ajanta caves near Aurangabad. These frescoes, which according to chemical analysis were done with a peculiar mixture of cow-dung plaster and white gypsum, fill the walls of 30 square monastic cells that are carved into a crescent-shaped cliff. They are remarkable not only for their graceful rendering and early use of perspective (many small figures are placed behind a large central one thus creating the illusion of depth), but for the exquisite stone carvings surrounding them. The frescoes depict the life of the Buddha as well as tales from the *Jatakas,* stories of Buddha's noble deeds in his previous incarnations. The oldest of these frescoes dates from the first century A.D., though work on the others continued for 700 years. When rediscovered in the nineteenth century many of the paintings were in a state of decay. Restored through the years, today they rank as one of India's most popular tourist attractions.

107

▲ Lustration and Renunciation, *Mahajanaka Jataka.*
Cave 1, second half of 6th century

Gothic Cathedrals

The Gothic style is noteworthy not only for its beauty but for its unique architectural innovations which, rapidly appearing on the European front in the early twelfth century, seemed to owe inspiration to no other precedents than the genius of its inventors. Previously, cathedrals were built with horizontal emphasis —heavy fortresslike structures with massive wall surfaces and few windows. Then in 1137 Abbot Suger began construction on the Church of St. Denis near Paris, a type of building never before seen in Europe. Within 50 years this new style reached full bloom.

Perhaps the greatest invention of the Gothic was the "flying buttress." Before the twelfth century walls were supported by thick columns and mammoth stone blocks. Now the buttress, a free-standing curved pillar, supported the wall from the *outside* like scaffolding, thus freeing designers to raise the height of the walls and to greatly increase windowspace. All the outer thrust of the wall, once so limiting, was absorbed by these external supports with ease. But this was only one of **108** many new features. Along with the buttress came the use of

ribbed vaulting, stained glass, arched windows, octagonal spires, facades covered with exquisite decorations of a heavily sculptural design. The whole organization presented such an uplifting sensation that one poet referred to a Gothic church as "frozen music."

Gothic cathedrals can be found throughout England, Germany, Spain, Italy, and the Netherlands. The finest, most agree, are in France. Chartres Cathedral with its broad nave, uniquely colored stained glass, famous sculptured facade, and quadripartite vaulting is generally considered the apotheosis of Gothic creation. In Paris, Notre Dame is known for its Rose Window and for its harmonious exterior. The cathedrals of Reims and Amiens are almost shockingly slender and vertical in feeling, and both make wonderful use of the cross-ribbed ceiling. The twin towers of Laon Cathedral, square at the base, octagonal at top, and crowned by a herd of cattle carved between the upper pillars, is perhaps the most individualistic of all the structures. The beauty of these cathedrals is that while all follow the same architectural scheme, improvisation within this scheme makes each unique.

109

▲ Notre Dame ▲ Stained-glass windows, Notre Dame

Machu Picchu

Machu Picchu, an Inca city discovered by the American explorer Hiram Bingham in 1911, is famous not only for the splendor of its ruins but for its fairytalelike setting 2,000 feet (600 m) high on a narrow, grassy ridge of the Andes Mountains near Cuzco, Peru. The city itself seems to grow out of its granite rock foundation, its buildings constructed with perfectly fitting rocks. This shows that the Incas were among the greatest stoneworkers the world has known. Though many of the buildings are today in a state of ruin, archeologists have identified private houses, stairways, terraces (agriculture was supported along the ridge by a highly sophisticated system of terracing and irrigation), stone basins, and baths. The world's finest example of an Inca *intihuatana,* or sun dial, is also here, used both for astronomical calculations and as part of the ritual of sun worship. The discovery of innumerable female skeletons belonging to a cult of virgin priestesses indicates that sun worship was in fact the *raison d'être* for this city, and it has been surmised that only those dedicated to the service of the Inca gods were allowed to reside here.

The Taj Mahal

Shah Jahan, fifth ruler in the line of Indian Mogul kings, had a favorite wife, Mumtaz Mahal, who died in the city of Agra giving birth to her fourteenth child. The grief-stricken king vowed to build a magnificent tomb to her in testimony of his love, and in the year 1632 construction began. Builders from across the Moslem world were invited to Agra. There were masons from Persia, calligraphers from Arabia, stonecutters from China, gardeners from Afghanistan, and even a master of mosaics from Italy. The name of the architect himself is not recorded, though credit for the final plans is usually given one Ustad Isa. For 22 years 20,000 men labored on this enormous mosquelike structure. Its magnificent dome, arched windows, subsidiary cupolas, and white marble facade rest on a huge platform surrounded by four marble towers.

Shah Jahan next planned to build himself a duplicate of this tomb in black across the river, and connect the two with a silver bridge. Before his plans materialized, however, he was deposed and exiled by his own son. Placed into confinement in the Red Fort across the river from the Taj Mahal, he passed his last days gazing at his magnificent monument. **111**

The Sphinx

Near the pyramids of Giza stands a famous Egyptian monument, the Sphinx. This imposing figure, whose body is that of a recumbent lion and whose face is that of a man, was built during the reign of King Khafre around 2250 B.C. and was considered ancient even to later dynasties of Egyptians. Constructed of limestone blocks each one some three times larger than the blocks used in the pyramids, scholars believe the sphinx to have originally been a symbol of Egyptian royalty (the name "Sphinx" is derived from the Egyptian *seshepanky*, meaning "living image").

The motif of the sphinx did not remain confined to the Egyptian world, but spread into the Mesopotamian Valley and beyond, eventually reaching Persia and later the medieval cathedrals, by then of course in altered form. The Greeks brought it to Thebes in 1600 B.C. under the name of Harmachis and made it possessor of the famous riddle of the Sphinx: what speaks with one voice, yet goes on four legs, then two, then three? This riddle, legend tells, was solved by Oedipus. Man, is the answer, for he crawls on four legs as a child, goes on two as an adult, and walks on three, his own plus a cane, when old.

112

Imperial Palace ▶

Kyoto

Many people know the Japanese city of Kyoto only as home of the Ryuanji Gardens. This arrangement of raked sand and carefully situated rocks is indeed unlike any other garden in the world. In it, its creator, the medieval monk-artisan, Soami, mirrored the Buddhist ideals of harmony and oneness. Few realize, however, it is only one of countless attractions in this city, which before 1868 was the capital of Japan. Kyoto has been the scene of numerous battles and devastations: razed in 976 A.D. and then again in 1477, it was restored to glory by several fifteenth- and sixteenth-century rulers. The Imperial Palace, longtime abode of the Japanese potentates, was rebuilt for the fourth time in 1854. Far older is the Shokokui, a monastery erected in 1382 which holds a large lecture hall and priceless works of art. The Togudo tea room, built in the late middle ages, is the prototype on which all Japanese tea rooms were modeled. Also in Kyoto are many of Japan's finest libraries, universities, theaters, shrines, and museums, as well as several important textile and ceramic centers.

5 Wonders of Mankind: Inventions

If we were to chart the number of years man has existed on this earth we would first draw a line a hundred feet long, then segment off an area less than a half-inch in length at the end of this line. The hundred feet would represent the total span of life on earth. The half-inch would be the era of man.

It is remarkable that during this brief stay mankind has been able to change the face of the planet so greatly. At first these changes were carried out by the use of basic tools—the wheel, the plow, the axe. With the Industrial Revolution, however, a string of inventions unprecedented in their wide-scale power for both construction and destruction appeared, among them the airplane, television, computer, and automobile. Each of these and others like it would be a wonder; and each, for better or worse, would cause an alteration not only in the earth itself, but in man's very view of that earth and of himself upon it.

▲ General Dynamics F-111 ▼ Cathode ray tube for early camera

◄ Early Mayan hieroglyphics ▼ IBM computer

The Wheel

One of the characteristics distinguishing man from animal is his ability to use a tool, and it is often said that of all man's tools the most significant is the wheel. Like many great inventions, the notion is simple yet so subtle that its principles eluded many sophisticated civilizations. The earliest wheels were found in the Mesopotamian Valley, dating from 4000 B.C., although these were potter's wheels, not used for conveyance at all. The first wheels were solid, made of radiated wooden planks clasped together by long pieces of copper and rimmed with studded iron hoops. Tree trunks sliced into round segments were also used. It was not until the second millennium B.C. that the Turks and Persians improved this cumbersome arrangement. Now with spokes a wheel could be lighter, bear more weight, and endure greater punishment. By 1000 B.C. there was a wide variety of vehicles: chariots, wheeled plows, merchants' carts, carriages. Later, other uses for the wheel were found, resulting in the millstone, spinning wheel, windmill, water wheel, clock gears, to name a few.

Maps

From earliest times men have tried to render the contours of their universe to scale. The first maps, however, were not really models of the physical world but gave symbolic delineation to religious and cosmological ideals. Even in the Middle Ages maps showed the cosmos bordered by endless oceans and by the celestial spheres. During these years mariners depended on stars for navigation.

Then in Europe around 1500 there was a spectacular renaissance of cartography—due in part to the great voyages of discovery that were taking place and the invention of the printing press. Up to this time the problem in mapping was transposing the image of the earth's curved surface onto a flat plane. Gerhard Mercator, a Belgian, solved this dilemma with a "projection" system of latitude and longitude. Now, by simply checking the coordinate points at the meeting of these two lines, one might never lose his way. In his famous *Atlas*, published in 1589, the art of modern cartography was born. In the centuries that followed all varieties of maps—those used for military purposes, navigation, meteorology, statistics, history, or ethnographic analysis—were in some way all heir to Mercator's ingenious device.

117

◀ Water wheel ▲ Map published in 1641 based on Mercator's projections

The Printing Press

Though few realize it, the printing press, or more accurately, moveable type, was invented in second-century China, where it was used to print Buddhist and Confucian texts. Not until 1456 did printing arrive in the West, the invention of a German, Johann Gutenberg, whose first book, now called the Gutenberg Bible, is still the most valuable printed item of all time.

Printing spread rapidly in Europe: within 30 years France, Italy, and Austria all had presses. William Caxton brought the art to England in 1471, setting up the first machines inside Westminster Abbey. By 1500 printing was an established art—and business—throughout Europe. Now a book that might have taken a monastic scribe several months or even years to copy by hand could be mechanically reproduced in a matter of days. The effect on Europe's political, artistic, educational, and intellectual life was profound.

118

The Franklin Press, ca. 1768 ▲

The earliest presses were run on the "vinepress" system, whereby a wheel set onto a screw was turned by hand, forcing an inked block of type onto a page of paper or parchment. (Using this technique woodblock engravings were also mass produced, greatly enhancing the engraver's art as well as the printer's.) The wheelpress was standard printing equipment until 1800 when the Earl of Stanhope introduced a model that worked by levers alone. This opened the door to a number of innovations, including Friedrich Konig's steam-driven press with self-inking rollers patented in 1810 (it was the first to print a newspaper, the *London Times*), and Richard Hoe's middle-of-the-century rotary press (using rotating cylinders it was capable of producing 8,000 pages an hour). In the twentieth century the development of offset lithography and rotogravure further increased printing capacity. Today certain machines are capable of printing 60,000 copies of 125-page newspapers in less than an hour.

119

▲ Multicolor web offset press

The Abacus

The abacus is the oldest computer known to man. It is a counting device still preferred by many people over more modern methods of calculation. The elementary abacus is a rectangular frame in which ten parallel rods or wires are fastened, and on which nine metal or wooden counters are strung. Each of the rods represents a numerical unit—either tens, hundreds, thousands, etc. The counters are manipulated in various ways along the rows, sometimes with unbelievable rapidity, and the answers are instantly readable in the configurations of the beads. Though most people assume the abacus to be Chinese, it is actually an ancient Babylonian invention. During the Renaissance when the Roman system of numbers was replaced by the decimal, the abacus, similarly based on the Roman method, died out and was last used in seventeenth-century Germany. The Orient was not so quick to lose this valuable instrument, however, and still today in Japan, China, and Indochina it is employed both as a device to teach children the rudiments of counting and as a calculator for the most sophisticated mathematical equations.

Twentieth-century Chinese abacus ▲ Ship's compass from mid-1800s ▶

The Compass

The oldest of all navigational tools and still the most important is the compass, an instrument known to man from the Middle Ages and, some theorize, long before. Mention of the compass officially appears for the first time in an eleventh-century Chinese manuscript. Whether it was actually invented in China, however, is debatable, for medieval Arabs, Greeks, and Scandinavians all employed its basic principle, this principle being that a piece of loadstone or magnetized iron placed in free suspension will invariably orient itself to a north-south axis, aligning with the magnetic poles of the earth.

The earliest compasses were simple pieces of loadstone or magnetized pins floated in water. Later, needles were placed on pins and allowed to pivot freely in the polar directions, a notion that has not changed much to this day (modern navigational compasses, though made with gyroscopes or prisms, adhere to the same principle). Using such indicators, navigational direction could be ascertained with total confidence and accuracy. The effect on world trade and migration was enormous, culminating in the Age of Discovery and the colonization of the New World.

Computers

The computer is a mechanical brain of extraordinary capacity; it can solve a problem in ten minutes that might take several trained scientists months to figure out. Yet the computer is based on the simplest of concepts—the choice between yes and no. What the computer does is to make a series of decisions between closing a circuit or leaving it open. It does not really think, at least not creatively. It either allows or disallows a process known in mathematics as "binary phenomena" to take place. And on this notion alone are based the most sophisticated calculations.

There are two types of computers: The "analog" works with abstract concepts like electrical potential, giving answers analogous to the quantities in a given problem. The "digital" computer negotiates discrete values, usually numbers.

The earliest computers were analogs, used for the prediction of tides. Lord Kelvin's model of 1872 is the most famous. Today many varieties are in wide use, some for broad-scale analysis, others for the most specific kinds of problem solving. Of all modern inventions, no other makes so much information available in so short a time.

Boomerangs

The boomerang, that ingenious arc-shaped wooden missile invented by the Australian aborigine, has fascinated and mystified man for years. If thrown properly (it must be held above and behind the shoulder, then tossed with a sharp, upward flick of the wrist), the boomerang inevitably comes back to its sender. This behavior is determined by a combination of the boomerang's spin and its "angle of incidence" when thrown.

A well-designed boomerang is capable of soaring distances of over 50 yards (46 m) or more before beginning its return flight. With some varieties the return may be a direct one, but more commonly it is rehearsed in a series of circles, sometimes three or four, the missile coming closer and closer to its source with every pass. Though the boomerang is still thrown in parts of western Australia—for hunting, as a decoy for hawks, to train soldiers in the art of weapon dodging, in competitive tournaments—it is nonetheless estimated that with the rapid urbanization of aboriginal tribes the truly skillful use of this remarkable weapon will soon be lost.

123

▲ Australian aborigine and boomerang
◄ Recent IBM computer using "monolithic" memory technology

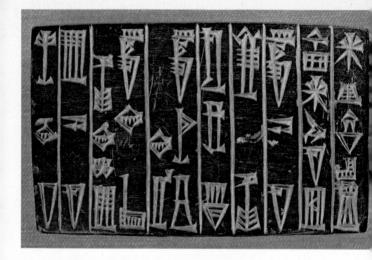

Writing

For untold centuries humanity passed down information by means of oral recitation alone. The village storyteller, the community leader, the priest, were all endowed with powerful memories and a storehouse of mnemonic devices. Then during the third century B.C. the Sumerians began to record transactions, both personal and commercial, in written signs. Now information could be codified, duplicated, and preserved.

This earliest writing was called cuneiform and consisted of a series of symbols, each representing a particular word or idea (a technique known as "syllabic" writing). The technique spread throughout the ancient world, resulting in the Egyptian script, the Hittite, and the Chinese (three other ancient languages, the proto-Elamite, proto-Indic, and Cretan, have never been deciphered). Around 2000 B.C. a second innovation was made, the alphabet. Created by the Greeks, it used actual letters rather than symbols, these letters representing sounds instead of ideas and having specific values as vowels and consonants. The number of signs thus required in a script was vastly reduced, and a more direct relationship between word and sound was established.

124

Black stone tablet, Iraq, about 2065 B.C. ▲ Wall telephone, 1913 ▶

Telephones

Though many believe the telephone was the creation of Alexander Graham Bell, its actual inventor was Philip Reis, a German engineer who in 1861 presented a primitive sending-receiving mechanism to the Physical Society of Frankfort which he named the "Telephone." Bell's contribution was actually a device capable of carrying the human voice. Patented in 1876, it was quickly improved upon by Edison and others, so that by 1920 general service was established throughout the United States.

Early phones operated on the principle of an electric impulse sent through a wire and converted into recognizable sound patterns at the other end. Early systems worked only over short distances and only a single call could be carried along the wire at a time. This was improved with the introduction of the amplifier, which strengthened the electrical signal at intervals along the wire, and also with so-called "carrier modulation," a process of electrical engineering which allowed almost indefinite numbers of frequencies to pass within a single circuit. Only 60 years after its invention the telephone spanned the world.

Airplanes

Many have wondered how an airplane, that massive collection of metal and steel, remains suspended in the air. The answer is found in the plane's forward movement. As the vehicle is pulled ahead by its propellers (or pushed by jet propulsion) pressure against the top of the wing decreases. The greater the plane's speed the less this pressure becomes. Finally, when the upward thrust beneath the plane is greater than the drag of its own weight, it becomes airborne.

Since the dawn of civilization men have yearned to fly. A Greek myth tells of the youthful Icarus whose wax wings melted when he disregarded his father's instructions and flew too near the sun. In Hindu myth heroes fly in magic chariots while in the Middle East the vehicle of lore was a flying carpet. By the seventeenth century men were determined to become airborne, and that same century a Frenchman, Bernier, built a winged contraption that safely carried him 30 feet (9 m) through the air. Credit for the first true manned and motor-propelled flight, however, belongs to Orville and Wilbur Wright. In 1903 their motor-driven plane flew a distance of **126** 852 feet (260 m) at Kitty Hawk, North Carolina.

Concorde, one of the fastest supersonic transports ▲

Clocks

In earlier centuries the measurement of time was less critical than today. Time was gauged on an approximate basis, tracked by the movements of the sun and by the changing seasons. Not until the modern age with its emphasis on precision and regularity did *exact* measurements of time become required. True, there were early implements such as the sundial in ancient Egypt and the waterclock in China; Plato invented a machine that indicated the hours upon an organ pipe, and Archimedes made a clockwork of springs and weights. These were experiments, however, novelties in their day. It was not until the Middle Ages that a timepiece based on modern mechanical principles was used, these principles being the moving of geared wheels by the power of an uncoiling spring or by the gradual falling of a weight regulated by a swinging pendulum. The first-known clock was built in Salisbury Cathedral, England, in 1386. It worked by means of an oscillating bar, a forerunner of the pendulum. So popular was this timepiece that other cathedrals incorporated clocks into their towers and naves, and by the sixteenth century domestic timepieces could be found in homes across Europe. **127**

▲ French mantle clock, late 1800s

The Zero

Many mathematicians consider the invention of the zero to be the greatest of all mathematical advancements. The zero belongs to the decimal system, originally devised in India in the third century B.C. The decimal system is based on the number ten: nine signs plus the all-important zero. The integers are arranged in linear order, each unit being ten times the magnitude of the unit next smaller. A small dot called a "decimal" is used whenever fractions are involved, each decimal division also indicating a multiple or power of ten. Moreover, for those places where a power of a base does not actually occur yet has to be numerically expressed the zero is employed, thus allowing the empty places in a calculation to be meaningfully represented. Without the zero the decimal system would be impossible; without the decimal system people would still be working with Roman numerals or even more clumsy systems of mathematical expression.

Microscopes

The microscope was to natural and physical sciences what the telescope was to astronomy—an instrument that brought science out of the range of speculation and into that of empirical fact. Although crude forms of microscopic enlargement had been used by the Greeks, the first instrument with some degree of magnification was invented by Zacharias Janseen in 1590. This was the "compound microscope," a handsome machine equipped with convex lens at the eyepiece, concave lens at the objective, and with a magnifying power of several hundred power. Through the years many improvements were made upon this early model including stronger lenses, and the binocular eyepiece, invented in 1902. Undoubtedly the greatest advancement, however, was the electron microscope, developed during the 1930s in Germany, an instrument that relied on high-velocity electrons rather than optical reflection for its resolving power. Using this wonder a hitherto unseen world was revealed; for the first time man peered into the inner tissue of the world around him, examining the very **128** building blocks of the physical universe.

Electron microscope ▶

Photography

Like so many of our greatest technological advancements, the principles of photography were understood centuries before its actual invention. For example, in 1600 it was known that silver chloride darkens when exposed to light, a curious fact but scarcely one to arouse much excitement. Not until the nineteenth century were the possibilities of this phenomenon recognized when Thomas Wedgwood first experimented with the exposure of images on a special paper treated with silver nitrate. Wedgewood's pictures were something of a novelty, especially since their image fàded several hours after they were taken. A French chemist, Joseph Niepce, carried the process one step further by inventing a means of permanently fixing this image onto a metal plate, a process he called "heliography."

In 1829 Niepce met Louis Daguerre and together they developed the "daguerrotype." This was a coated metal plate designed to be exposed to light within a square cell called a "camera" (after the Latin *camera obscura* meaning "dark box"). The plate was then developed in a dark room with vapors of mercury. Though many improvements were subsequently made on this technique, Daguerre's invention truly marked the beginning of modern photography.

The possibilities of this medium were far from exhausted with the still camera, however. In the latter part of the nineteenth century people began wondering why it was not possible to animate images as well as to fix them. Finally in 1890 Thomas Edison invented a working technique and patented it. It was his "Kinetoscope," a camera system in which sequences of photographs were projected onto a screen by means of an intense light and a magnifying lens. The Edison Company soon began marketing improved versions of this machine; by the first decade of the next century moving pictures, too, were part of the modern technological world.

▲ Daguerreotype camera made in 1839 by Giroux

Tools

A fundamental trait distinguishing man from animal is his ability to conceive of, to build, and to use a tool. Indeed, the very term ''Stone Age'' is derived from the fact that man's earliest societies were founded on the use of stone tools, the most primitive being blunt ax heads, poking and striking implements, the more advanced being adz blades, bifacial cutting instruments, and arrowheads.

Use of the tool helped make mankind truly human; it enabled him to become creative towards his environment—to build, to alter, to invent, rather than to be a simple recipient of nature's forces like other animals. Already by the Bronze Age, his implements were highly developed. The craftsmen who built the Egyptian pyramids possessed the secrets of the iron-headed mallet, the saw, the chisel, the plane, the drill, and various measuring devices. The Romans used most of the hand tools known to us today, and though improved through the years, some eventually motorized and electrified, the basic **132** principles have remained the same.

Early American tools ▲
(Front) Edison lamp, ca. 1880; (back) Swan experimental lamp, 1878 ▶

Electric Light

Man has made use of many ingenious systems to light his home and town—from the early oil lamps and tallow candles to the gaslights that later lined the streets of Europe and America. It was electricity, however, that lit the world.

Though it was known as early as 1600 that illumination could be produced by creating certain forms of electric agitation, it was not until the nineteenth century that Thomas Edison, employing principles developed by several Russian and English inventors, created the first serviceable electric light. This was made by passing a current of electricity through a resisting medium, in this case a carbonized thread sealed in a glass bulb. The thread was then rendered incandescent and would remain alight 600 hours, the result of over 1,200 experiments. Following Edison's creation other light systems similarly appeared, each serving a different function. The arc light was used for large-wattage lamps such as those used to make films. Fluorescent lamps brought illumination to commercial and private spaces, while gaseous vapor lamps provided more unusual kinds of lighting effects like sun lamps and black light.

Radio and Television

The miracles of radio and television are due to the same phenomena: the radiation and detection of electromagnetic waves. By the end of the nineteenth century Clerk Maxwell and others had already discovered that any electrical disturbance caused so-called "radio waves" to radiate into space. These waves belonged to the electromagnetic spectrum, and were hence universal. Could they be sent and received without wires at all? Guglielmo Marconi, the Italian inventor and engineer, thought so, and in 1895, using primitive electrical apparatus, he transmitted radio impulses a distance of nine miles (14.5 km) through the air, overnight revolutionizing world communications.

In the years that followed, key improvements were added to Marconi's "wireless," such as the arc oscillator, the antenna, and especially the electron tube, which made it possible to amplify a voice with perfect accuracy. By 1920 radio was sophisticated enough for national broadcasting. Essentially the **134** radio consists of a sender, a receiver, and a medium of propa-

gation. A voice is projected into a transmitter causing sound vibrations. These are broken down to radio energy and carried on waves through the air to a receiver. The receiver decodes the impulses, reassembles them until they duplicate the original, and amplifies them. This same technique was then applied to the problem of television. If it was possible to transmit sound, reasoned scientists, why not visual images too? Light waves were also part of the electromagnetic spectrum. What was needed, was some kind of apparatus to transform this light into electricity. This was to be the photoelectric cell. Designed by A. A. Campbell Swinton in 1908 and perfected 18 years later by the Englishman, J. L. Baird, who was the first to electrically transmit animated images, the photoelectric cell was a kind of converting machine that turned light images into pulsating electric currents. These currents were then conducted to a station, amplified, superimposed on radio carrier waves, and broadcasted. In this way a single picture could be multiplied indefinitely; thus began the age of telecommunications.

Space Flight

On July 20, 1969, two American astronauts landed on the moon. Though the event caused worldwide amazement, the dream of space exploration was in fact as old as man himself. Early Navaho myths told of travelers arriving from other planets by a meteor. But during the Enlightenment men first began to make empirical observations of what was beyond this planet: the telescope was invented, various laws of motion were propounded by Newton and Galileo, Kepler calculated the orbits of the planets. This foundation led to greater technological advances in the nineteenth century, so that by the middle of the twentieth, manned space flight was a potential reality. The problem, of course, was building a missile strong enough to escape from the earth. This dilemma was overcome by the invention of high-speed jet rockets with enough thrust to exceed gravitational inertia; also by "staging," whereby the rocket was assembled in ejectable sections, each carrying a separate supply of fuel for different segments of the journey. These concepts plus calculations for flight trajectory, navigation, and acceleration rates all contributed to eventual success in space.

The Plow

Man first began to cultivate the earth around 10,000 B.C. For many centuries methods of cultivation were so primitive, limited to digging sticks and chopping tools, that man still maintained a seminomadic way of life, working the land until it was depleted and then moving on.

The plow first appeared in the Eastern Mediterranean around 3000 B.C. and quickly spread throughout the ancient world. It was a simple instrument, made up of a "share point" that cut into the ground, a "moldboard" to which the share was mounted, a "beam" to draw the share, and handles behind to guide the whole mechanism. Sometimes pushed by a man, sometimes drawn by a beast of burden, the plow cut deeply into the earth, breaking up the soil, turning it so that new surfaces were continually exposed to sun and air, and chopping up weeds in the process to fertilize the area. The ground no longer became exhausted after several growing seasons, and the result was that mankind began to settle down. Towns arose, cities, then entire civilizations, all centered on a farm economy and based on the agricultural advancements allowed by one ingenious tool. **137**

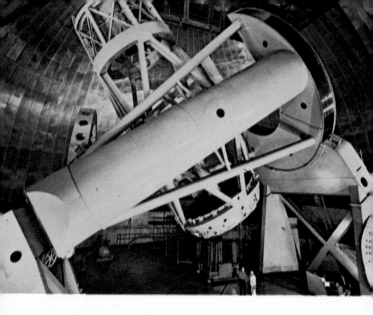

Telescopes

Modern astronomy began with the invention of the telescope. This wonderful instrument was first made in Holland by Hans Lippershey, a spectacle-maker who one day in 1608 happened to hold two lenses in alignment and noticed that they magnified a far-off weathervane. Lippershey then placed the lenses in a tube and trained them on the landscape, inventing the first telescope. Two years later Galileo used it to discover the satellites of Jupiter and to find sun spots.

The earliest telescopes, called ''refractors,'' depended on lens enlargement alone. Such mechanisms were fraught with image distortion and required enormous optical extensions to get a clear picture. Isaac Newton improved this by inventing the ''reflecting'' telescope, which first captured the stellar image on a mirror and then transmitted it to the eyepiece. The mirror greatly increased the size of the image and at the same time concentrated a greater intensity of light, rendering the image far more distinct. Improvements in the telescope were rapid, leading to the development of the giant 200-inch (508-cm) mirror telescope atop Mt. Palomar, the largest of its kind in **138** the United States.

Hale Telescope, Mt. Palomar, California ▲ Stock racing car ▶

Automobiles

The notion of a self-propelled vehicle had been considered long before the time of Henry Ford. Roger Bacon, a thirteenth-century monk, spoke of cars that "move at inestimable speed without animals to draw them." Leonardo da Vinci drew plans for a self-moving cart; and in 1760 J. H. Genevois designed a vehicle propelled by windmills. These and other early conceptions lacked one essential ingredient: the internal combustion engine.

The automobile was the creation of many men, but foremost was a German named Carl Benz. In the later part of the nineteenth century Benz built a gas-fired machine and drove it around a track four times before it fell to pieces. Gottlieb Daimler, a gunsmith, further developed Benz's ideas, building cars with motors that revolved at 900 r.p.m. and others with four-speed capacity. At the turn of the century Henry Ford entered the field. It was Ford's genius to see the potentiality of mass marketing the automobile. Previously the auto had been a novelty for the rich. With the production of the Model A in 1908 and with the establishment of stations to service it, Ford put the automobile within buying range of the middle class.

6 Wonders of Mankind: Art

Mankind expresses wonder for the world through the medium of art. All civilizations, all ages, all people at all times have had a form of art—it is a universal practice. This art of course varies tremendously from culture to culture: the wall paintings at Lascaux, a medieval Chinese scroll painting, an American Indian rug, a modern sculpture. None of these things would at first seem to have much in common. But they do, for all are attempts to demonstrate our sense of awe and emotion before the vast world around us. The following works of art are a sampling of the most successful attempts.

Book of Hours,
15th century France;
Belles Heures of Jean,
Limbourg ▶

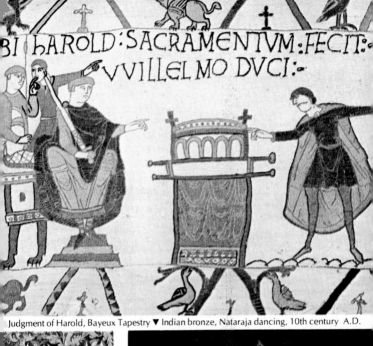

BI HAROLD:SACRAMENTVM:FECIT:
VVILLELMO DVCI:·

Judgment of Harold, Bayeux Tapestry ▼ Indian bronze, Nataraja dancing, 10th century A.D.

Lascaux Cave Paintings

In 1868 some railway workers near Les Eyzies, France, un-
earthed a strange discovery: five ancient skeletons soon to be
dubbed by archeologists "Cro-Magnon Man." These findings
turned out to be the remains of an extensive and highly intelligent race of early man, one that used stone tools, built shelters,
hunted with spears, performed ceremonial worship, and most
unusual of all, practiced art, the first example of such an
activity among primitive humanity. Examples included
mother goddesses carved in stone, tracings on ivory and bone,
and elegant wall paintings, the best examples being those in
the Lascaux Caves near Montignac. Here extensive murals
some 30,000 years old show a panoply of deer, oxen, horses,
and lesser game. Some are brightly colored in an extraordinarily durable temperalike paint. Several figures, especially the
bulls, are drawn on a large scale, while others are small,
half-completed, and even sketchy. Archeologists have long
theorized the purpose of these works. It is generally believed
that the figures were drawn for magical functions: a picture of
a deer sets up a sympathetic relationship with the real animal,
thus assuring its capture during the day's hunt.

Oriental Carpets

Though many well-known varieties of rugs exist throughout the world, those produced on the continent of Asia are the most coveted. In Asia each country and, in turn, each town, has its own variety of weave and ornament that make its product unique. In Turkey the well-known Ghiordes rug, woven in the town of Ghiordes, is made with bright, strongly contrasting colors, numerous borders, and strong, thick knotting. Daghestan rugs from the Caucasus show unusual mosaic-like shapes with brightly colored diagonal bands. In Persia Kerman rugs employ bird and animal images, while those from Hamadan display dark medallions and are mostly made from camel's hair. Rugs in the East are manufactured on hand looms. Specially dyed yarns of cotton, silk, or wool are stretched across a frame and woven in row upon row of tiny knots. Sometimes entire towns work on a single rug, and sometimes the rug may be so large that it takes several years to finish. Once completed, however, an authentic oriental rug is not only a thing of beauty and function, but may last as long as three or four hundred years without wearing thin.

143

▲ Kashan Persian silk and silver rug, 17th century

The Mona Lisa

Unquestionably the most famous painting in the world is Leonardo da Vinci's *Mona Lisa.* Considered priceless even in its own time, this picture is visited by more than a million people a year in the Louvre. Novels, critiques, even operas have used it as a subject. Yet what is it about this simple portrait of a Florentine merchant's wife that so captured the imagination of mankind? It must be recalled that in the Middle Ages the human face was usually depicted in an idealized and stylized manner, and that portraiture for its own sake was rare, especially for the commoner. This precedent maintained itself even up to the early Renaissance. So when in 1503 Leonardo created on canvas the image of a real person—a woman of flesh and blood, and a beautiful one at that, with a mysterious smile, graceful hand-clasp and half-turned body (something new in the technique of figure painting)—viewers for the first time felt themselves in the presence of a living human being, but one with distinct individual qualities. This blending of the universal with the particular is one reason why audiences have so long held the *Mona Lisa* in awe.

144

Detail ▲ Centaur and Lapith Fighting ▶

The Elgin Marbles

A temple in ancient Greece was built not as a hall for a congregation but as a space to house the gods themselves. Thus the marble carvings in the Parthenon were sacred in their own right, incarnations of divinity in stone. These stones portrayed various Attic deities at war, play, and adventure. On the east pediment one could see Athena and Poseidon contesting the guardianship of Athens. Only a few fragments still remain from this portion, including a torso of Athena and one of Iris, her lady-in-waiting. The carvings of the west pediment fared better: the recumbent figure of Dionysus taking wine is one of the great masterpieces of ancient art, as is the horse's head from the chariot of the moon. Various friezes and metopes show battle scenes, cavalrymen on parade, sacrifices, and a range of mythological scenes.

In 1803 most of these carvings lay scattered at the base of the Parthenon, broken and neglected. They were then brought to England and installed in the British Museum. Their procurement was the work of Lord Elgin; and hence these great works have come to be known as the Elgin Marbles.

Picasso Sculpture

Perhaps no man has ever had a more profound impact on the world of Western art than Pablo Picasso. One of the features that has made this Spanish master's art so influential is his insistence that the viewer see his work with an unconditioned eye.

Stifled by the vapid realism of nineteenth-century academic painting, Picasso carried on the work of the Impressionists and Post-Impressionists by depicting the world in stylized, interpretative, and nonliteral terms, a new approach to painting in the West. Early in the twentieth century Picasso and his associates stunned the art community by producing works in which several simultaneous views of a single three-dimensional object were juxtaposed onto a flat canvas, thus displaying several different views of the same item on a plane surface. The technique was known as "Cubism." Its effects are still being felt today, for it is now well established that in order to capture the essence of an object slavish detail-for-detail reproduction is not required.

A further attempt to sharpen the viewer's sensitivities was initiated in the 1930s when Picasso began incorporating "found" or commonplace articles into his art. In his sculpture *Baboon and Young,* we see a round-bodied mother ape holding a baby to her breast. The statue, 21 inches (53 cm) high and cast in bronze, is a rather droll subject for a work of art. Further inspection proves the piece to be even more unconventional: the motherly face of the baboon is a child's toy automobile embedded into the casting. This discovery is at once humorous and startling. As was Picasso's intent, the viewer is forced to perceive the work in a new way, a combination of the sublime and the commonplace, an amalgam of oddly coexisting realities. The result of using found objects in art was almost as influential as Cubism itself. Like Cubism, it contributed to a broadening of definitions concerning what was acceptable as a work of art.

▲ *Baboon and Young* ▼ *Three Musicians*

Medieval Book of Hours

In medieval Europe prayers were recited at designated times every day; the so-called "Book of Hours" provided the text for these prayers. Although popular during the twelfth century, examples of these books can be found as late as the sixteenth century, especially in Italy and France. One of the finest is the *Jeanne d'Evreux Book of Hours*. It was drawn by the artist, Jean Pucelle, in 1325 for his patron Charles IV of France, who in turn gave it to his wife, Jeanne d'Evreux. Typically small, measuring 3⅝ inches by 2⅜ inches (9 x 6.5 cm), the pages of this missal are alive with a parade of figures, not only those from religious passages such as the Psalms, the life of the Virgin and St. Louis, and the Passion of Christ, but with an array of humorous animals, strange clowns, dragons, knights, cooks, beggars, musicians, and acrobats. Hundreds of other caricatures filled the border of every page, these grotesqueries serving both as a kind of comic relief and as illustrations for moral fables well known to readers of the day. The total effect is one of harmony, beauty, and gentle humor, making it one of **148** the most treasured manuscripts from the later Middle Ages.

Jeanne d'Evreux Book of Hours; Annunciation ▲ Bas-relief of Mayet, detail ▶

Egyptian Sculpture

In order to understand the essence and power of ancient sculpture one must realize that early artists were working not for personal fame but for the glory of their gods. And in creating images of beings, whether gods or men, the purpose was not to capture a literal likeness or to create something beautiful, but to render in stone that element of immortality they believed to be present in all living things. Thus in the bas-relief of Mayet, now in the British Museum, this goddess of justice is portrayed not so much as an actual living person but as an idealized personification of the virtues she represents. On her head she wears an ostrich feather, symbol of truth and justice. Her expression is calm and impartial, two characteristics needed for objective judgment. The coloring, which has preserved itself so well through the millenniums (the pigment mixture used in many Egyptian polychromes has still not been chemically analyzed with success) is muted yet harmonious, while the hieroglyphics behind her, which describe her functions as divine judge in the afterlife, are arranged in neat composition perfectly combining the function of communicative script and esthetic design.

Giotto Fresco

Most chapters on Renaissance painting begin with the Florentine painter Giotto di Bondone. Though previously sublime, painting had become somewhat stylized and conventional in Giotto's time. Giotto changed all this within his lifetime (1266?–1337), introducing such elements to painting as the foreshortening of limbs, the plastic molding of features, and the use of light and shadow to produce depth; in short, he laid the groundwork for realism.

In *The Death of St. Francis,* a fresco mural in the Church of Santa Croce in Florence, his innovations are well illustrated. Giotto establishes a living tableau of figures here, not simply a static, ornamental arrangement. As the dying saint's soul is borne over the monastery walls his followers react with various postures of remorse and shock, just as they might under actual conditions. We seem to be peeking into an actual event, watching a drama unfold; and this illusion is heightened by the naturalism of the figures and faces themselves. This method of showing the world in a literal rather than symbolic manner was soon adopted by painters across Italy and within 50 years **150** the Renaissance in painting was underway.

Detail of *The Death of St. Francis* ▲ Indian miniature, 17th century ▶

The Peacock Throne

The most powerful dynasty ever to rule India were the Moguls, a royal lineage that came to power in the sixteenth century and retained absolute rule until displaced by the British four centuries later. For so mighty a group of sovereigns a magnificent throne was in order. This was the Peacock Throne, the *Takht-i-Taus,* the most richly decorated royal seat of all time. Constructed by Shah Jahan in 1628 (the same king who built the Taj Mahal), it was seen by many travelers through the years. One described it as a rectangular platform on which four studded pillars were situated, the capitals of each displaying two jeweled peacocks surrounding a diamond-leaved tree. These pillars supported a gold roof similarly encrusted with pearls, emeralds, and sapphires. The king sat beneath his precious canopy on a seat of silver and gems, having mounted the whole structure on a staircase of solid gold. To craft this amazing construction seven years and equivalent to fifty million dollars were required. Such a remarkable work was of course the object of much envy through the years. Finally in 1738 it was carried off to Persia where it quickly vanished.

Japanese Scroll Painting by Sesshu

Zen Buddhist scroll painting in Japan has inspired viewers for centuries, not only for the dexterity and beauty of style but for the great economy in which so much is said with so few strokes and lines. This is because in Zen the stress is on intuitive flashes of spiritual illumination rather than on scriptural or intellectual dogma. Its art exemplifies a sudden, direct quality. For example, in the scroll *Splash Ink Landscape,* the work of perhaps the most famous of all Japanese painters, Sesshū (1420–1506), we see a simple portrait of nature—a tree towers over a lonely human habitation. The technique used here, the so-called "splash ink" method, is done by the application of rapid, spontaneous brushstrokes inked on in so many subtle gradations of light and dark that they almost seem like random splashes. There is nothing accidental about this arrangement, however. The effect is fully unified and harmonious, providing a fleeting glance into the heart of nature, not only to stress the illusionary and transient quality of the world **152** but to imply the existence of a higher truth behind it.

Detail of *Splash Ink Landscape* ▲ *Siva Nataraja* ▶

Indian Bronze Statue

Few works of art are more graceful or expressive than a finely wrought Indian bronze statue. Cast by means of the ancient "lost-wax" process, the artist first models his figures in clay, then takes an impression of that figure in wax. The wax mold is covered with plaster and the whole piece is heated. The wax runs out through special holes, leaving its impression behind in the plaster covering. This covering then becomes the final mold used to cast the bronze.

In the hands of a skillful craftsman an Indian bronze will invariably demonstrate the four fundamental traits of Indian art as espoused in Hindu scriptures: "unity, vitality, infinity, and repose." The figure *Siva Nataraja* (Siva, King of Dancers), cast in south India in the twelfth century, is an excellent example. This statue shows the god Siva expressing through physical movement the interplay of life and death. He stands serenely poised on one leg, his lithe body trampling the dwarf of ignorance. His hands hold a flame and drum, symbols of sight and sound, while his features speak of creation and destruction alike, those cosmic processes with which Hindu art has always been concerned.

The Sistine Chapel

When Pope Julius II commissioned Michelangelo to paint the ceiling of the Sistine Chapel in 1523 it was simply to keep the great painter busy till blueprints for the pope's tomb could be made ready. Little did the pope realize that Michelangelo would extend the plans for this ceiling into a prodigious labor, and that in it he would attempt a synthesis of the entire cosmic order.

The design of the Sistine Chapel is based on fixed geometric shapes—the square, circle, and triangle—which were regarded as eternal forms in the philosophy of Neoplatonism to which Michelangelo was so attached. Within these geometric outlines the painter depicted a galaxy of men, supermen, and divine beings. He chronicled God's making of the universe, the creation and fall of Adam; he illustrated the story of Noah, David, and Solomon along with other Old Testament prophets; depicted a teeming collection of sibyls, angels, ancestors of Christ, common men, slaves, and young athletes twisting and turning in typical Michelangelesque manner— more than 300 figures in all. As seen from the floor, the effect of this ceiling fresco is one of almost supernatural unity, made all the more astounding by the fact that Michelangelo completed the whole work, all 10,000 square feet (3048 m), in four years, and that he completed it by himself without so much as the aid of an apprentice.

The Bayeux Tapestry

The Bayeux Tapestry depicts the conquest of Britain from the point of view of the Normans. Created in 1088 for the Cathedral of Bayeux, this masterpiece was originally designed to cover an unadorned panel of masonry running between the nave and triforium gallery of the cathedral. Measuring 231 feet (70.4 m) in length and only 20 inches (51 cm) in width, it is technically not a tapestry at all but an embroidery, an appliqué of colored yarns on stiff linen. Its purpose is to tell the story of William the Conqueror, the man who destroyed the English forces at the Battle of Hastings in 1066. We see William throughout the tapestry, participating in the events leading up to the battle and taking part in the battle itself. This tapestry, the product of an English embroidery guild, is extraordinary not only for its age, condition, and esthetic merits, but as a kind of living historybook in which the costumes, beliefs, and customs of eleventh-century medieval life are chronicled detail for detail before us.

Chinese Ritual Bronzes

Ancient Chinese craftsmen produced many swords, masks, and ornaments of bronze. Most importantly, they cast ritual vessels that today are perhaps the most sought after of all Chinese relics. Although the designs adorning these vessels have reappeared in Chinese art even up to the present, the majority of the vessels were crafted between 1500 B.C. and 100 A.D. Such vessels were used first by members of a family during a ritual feast. Then they were placed in the family chapel where they served as a shrine and as a sort of family tree (the names of the family members were inscribed on the object's flanks). The vessel, cast via the lost-wax process, was made in the shape of a food container, a bowl, jug, wine goblet, or cooking pot, all of which were symbolic of nourishment and growth. They were covered with arabesques depicting a variety of animal motifs and secret magical signs. As these vessels grew older, a soft green patina covered their surface. Veneration for these pieces is not just a modern fashion. Medieval records tell that the Duke of Chu once waged war against a nearby kingdom simply to capture his neighbor's collection of bronzes.

157

◀ Detail ▲ Pair of Yu (wine holders) from 11th century B.C.

Index

159

David Carroll is a freelance writer and author of thirteen books, including one on the Taj Mahal. A graduate of Harvard College, he spent two years in the Peace Corps in Nepal as curator of the Royal Nepal Museum. He catalogued the Henry Welcome Collection of Tibetan Art at the University of Southern California and since then has run several art galleries and a research organization.